Harlequin
romance
by Anne Mather
comes to life
on the movie screen

starring

KEIR DULLEA · SUSAN PENHALIGON

Leopard in the Snow

Guest Stars
KENNETH MORE · BILLIE WHITELAW

featuring GORDON THOMSON as MICHAEL
and JEREMY KEMP as BOLT

Produced by JOHN QUESTED and CHRIS HARROP
Screenplay by ANNE MATHER and JILL HYEM
Directed by GERRY O'HARA

An Anglo-Canadian Co-Production

OTHER
Harlequin Romances
by YVONNE WHITTAL

1915—EAST TO BARRYVALE
2002—THE SLENDER THREAD
2077—DEVIL'S GATEWAY
2101—WHERE SEAGULLS CRY
2128—THE PRICE OF HAPPINESS

Handful of Stardust

by

YVONNE WHITTAL

Harlequin Books

TORONTO • LONDON • NEW YORK • AMSTERDAM • SYDNEY

Original hardcover edition published in 1977
by Mills & Boon Limited

ISBN 0-373-02162-3

Harlequin edition published May 1978

Printed in U.S.A.

CHAPTER ONE

EXUBERANT voices and the loud twanging of electric guitars fought for supremacy as Samantha Little and Clive Wilmot faced each other on the dimly lit terrace of the hotel. Both were equally fair, but whereas Clive was tall and slender with his shoulders hunched in anger and his sensitive mouth petulant at that moment, Samantha stood small and erect, with an almost regal quality in the way she held herself. Except for the faint glimmer of tears in her large violet blue eyes, there was no way of guessing at the turbulent thoughts that were racing through her mind during that tense confrontation.

'Don't be such a puritan, Sam,' Clive Wilmot was saying accusingly. 'Be with it and let yourself go.'

'I'm afraid I can't let myself go to the extent you desire, Clive.'

'I thought you loved me.' His lips tightened once again with irritation and anger.

'I do love you, you know I do, and that's why I can't do what you ask of me.' She bit down hard on a trembling lower lip and fought for composure. 'I can't live with you, Clive, until after we're married.'

'But you know that marriage is out of the question at the moment.'

'I know that, Clive, and I understand, but until then you must respect my wishes.'

For several seconds he stared at her in angry disbelief before he straightened and said, 'I'm going back inside. Are you coming?'

Samantha shook her head. 'If you don't mind, I'd like to remain out here for a while longer.'

'Suit yourself,' he shrugged negligently, striding along the terrace and disappearing through the glass doors.

Samantha closed her eyes for a moment to relieve the ache behind them and tasted the salty tang of the sea on her lips. Clive's behaviour had been strange lately, and at times she glimpsed a side of his nature that did not entirely impress her. His anger and dissatisfaction never lasted long, and he usually succeeded in sweeping aside her fears by apologising profusely and kissing her warmly. His erring little boy act always touched her heart and vanquished her misgivings. He was also so terribly handsome.

Her high heels tapped softly on the stone floor as she walked along the terrace, which was on the third floor level, taking the opposite direction to the one Clive had taken until she eventually found her way barred by an iron gate. She clutched at it for a moment, tempted to go beyond it into the lush greenery of the garden bathed in moonlight which she had discovered so unexpectedly. While she was still contemplating whether to enter or retrace her steps, the decision was more or less taken for her when the gate squealed slightly and swung open beneath her agitated hands.

The Trydon Hotel sliced into the steep hill, and for the first time Samantha realised that the remaining portion of the hill on the east side was on a level with the third floor of the building, with a concrete bridge leading from a secluded balcony into the garden she had just entered.

She stood for a moment with her back pressed hard against the gate and inhaled the sweet fragrance of frangipani as it mingled with the tangy sea air on this sultry January night. The din of the party at the other end of the terrace barely reached her ears in the tranquillity and peace of the enchanting oasis she had stumbled upon. The grass was springy beneath her feet in this scented garden, the shadows soft and enfolding on such a starlight night as she wandered further. It respresented a way of escape from her troubled thoughts; a garden to dream in when harsh reality threatened one's sanity, she decided unhappily as she ventured deeper into the garden.

A dark shape disengaged itself from the shadows beside her and, startled, she turned and fled.

'Just a moment!' an imperious voice halted her in her stride before she reached the gate. She turned, pressing a hand against her throat where a frightened pulse throbbed achingly. A man was approaching her and in the moonlit darkness he seemed terrifyingly tall and broad-shouldered, his dark evening suit almost blending with the shadows. 'Did I startle you?'

His voice was pleasantly deep and somehow reassuring, she noticed as she stammered a reply. 'I—I thought I was the only one here.'

He laughed briefly. 'I've been watching you for some time. Are you a resident at this hotel, or were you escaping from the rowdy party in the restaurant?'

'I suppose you could saying I was escaping from the party,' she acknowledged guiltily.

A brief, uncomfortable silence lingered between them before he said calmly, 'I suppose you do realise you're trespassing?'

Samantha bit her lip nervously. 'Oh, dear! I should have known but I couldn't resist the temptation. Who does this garden belong to?'

'It belongs to the owner of this hotel.'

'You mean Brett Carrington, the man who owns al-

most half the five-star hotels in the Eastern Cape as well
as one of the most prosperous sheep farms in the
Karoo?' she asked incredulously, voicing her harassed
thoughts.

'That's rather a sweeping statement, but yes, it does
belong to Brett Carrington.' He coughed slightly.

'He's an extremely wealthy man, I hear,' Samantha
continued thoughtfully, loath to leave this paradise, yet
strangely disturbed by the man confronting her.

'Does wealth impress you?' he asked suddenly.

'Good heavens, no! I should imagine that being
wealthy could be an agonising bore, especially when
people fawn all over you.' What on earth was she doing,
she wandered crazily, talking to this stranger in the
shadows of this secluded garden as though she had
every right to be there? 'It must be terribly difficult for
Mr Carrington to know whether people are sincere, or
merely trying to cash in on his wealth.'

'Experience makes one a good judge of character.'

'I suppose so,' she agreed reluctantly. 'Do you know
him well?'

The tall, dark figure beside her moved slightly. 'You
could say I know him well. I am Brett Carrington.'

'Oh, lord!' she gasped, clapping her hand over her
mouth. 'I've said and done all the wrong things, I suppose.'

'Look, we can't talk here,' he said briskly his hand at
her elbow and sending a current of awareness along her
nerves. 'Let me take you inside, then I can at least offer
you something to drink before I return you to your
friends.'

'Oh, I don't think——'

'Have you lost your nerve?' he challenged, his face
an unrecognisable blur in the darkness.

'No, I haven't, but——'

'Come, then.' He led her across the garden and on to the balcony, opening the double glass doors and drawing aside the heavy curtains for her to enter. It was when those doors closed behind them that Samantha began to panic.

'Mr Carrington, I must apologise for entering your private garden uninvited, but I don't think I ought to make further use of your hospitality.'

'Relax, you're quite safe. I have some excellent sherry I can offer you,' he replied unperturbed, selecting a bottle from the teak cabinet at the other end of the room and filling two delicately stemmed glasses.

Samantha took this opportunity to glance about her and felt a pleasurable feeling of delight ripple through her at the plush gold furnishings and the quiet elegance of his impeccable taste.

Brett Carrington turned towards her then and she found herself looking directly into the dark brown eyes with peculiar gold flecks about the pupils. They were unusual eyes that seemed to burn through her with a strange intensity.

'Sit down,' he said as she accepted the glass of sherry from him, and she subsided thankfully into the nearest chair as she became aware of a strange weakness in her legs at his now disturbing nearness.

Her mind registered clearly for the first time the tanned angular face and thick dark hair greying at the temples. His suit was well cut and expensive, the white lacy front of his shirt contrasting drastically with the dark evening suit and black bow-tie. He was no longer a young man and neither was he old, she thought, hastily judging his age to be about thirty-five, and he looked different somehow from the photographs she had seen of him in the newspapers—more attractive, perhaps. But, with his rugged good looks, he could never be called handsome, although there was something undeniably authoritative about his distinguished manner and the arrogant set of his broad shoulders. It was his eyes, however, that filled her with the curious desire to escape.

'I don't know your name,' he interrupted her thoughtful scrutiny, and Samantha blushed, realising that she had been staring rudely.

'Samantha Little,' she replied warily.

His glance swept over her briefly and the hard smooth mouth twisted cynically. 'I dare say you've been teased enough about suiting your name, so may I call you Samantha?'

'Why ... yes, of course.' Startled by this request, she almost spilt some of the liquid on to her lap.

'Tell me about the party in the restaurant,' he said.

'My friend Gillian Forbes is celebrating her twenty-first birthday.'

'Did something happen to make you want to escape?'

He was far too astute, she realised and, to her surprise, found herself replying, 'I had a slight disagreement with my boy-friend.'

'I see.' His expression altered without warning and became coldly impersonal. 'You'd better drink up so I can return you to your friend before he comes looking for you.'

When he eventually walked her back to the restaurant, he took her through the garden once again and she turned at the gate to take one last look at the enchanting and slightly mysterious paradise. Against the wall beside the gate was a large board marked PRIVATE. Why she had not noticed it before she could not imagine, and she felt decidedly guilty at having trespassed into Brett Carrington's private domain.

'Oh, there's Clive!' she exclaimed as they entered the

noisy restaurant, and it was then that the most extra-ordinary thing happened.

Clive hesitated in his stride, paling visibly when he noticed her companion, but he recovered swiftly as he made his way towards them among the tables. A drastic change had taken place in Brett Carrington as well, she noticed. The polite, impersonal mask had been ripped from his face to be replaced by a look that was close to hatred, and there was a hardness about his mouth that chilled her to the marrow.

'So, Clive Wilmot, we meet again,' Brett Carrington remarked drily while Clive regained his composure with a visible effort. 'I've had the pleasure of your young lady's company for a few short moments.'

'So I see,' Clive muttered nervously.

'I'm afraid I wandered into Mr Carrington's private garden by mistake,' Samantha explained hastily, her cheeks suffused with colour as Clive glanced at her questioningly.

'So there you are, Sam,' Gillian interrupted this tense little scene as she and Stan fought their way through the dancing guests towards them. 'Stan and I have been looking everywhere for you, and so has Clive.'

'Mr Carrington,' Samantha began almost apologetically, 'this is my friend Gillian Forbes and her fiancé, Stan Dreyer.'

Brett Carrington acknowledged their presence with a polite nod. Clive stepped past him at that moment and placed a possessive arm about Samantha's shoulders, but Brett Carrington merely raised a mocking eyebrow in their direction before giving his complete attention to Gillian.

'I believe it's your twenty-first birthday,' he said politely. 'May I also offer my congratulations?'

Gillian thanked him with equal politeness, and in

the same easy manner asked: 'Would you care to join us, Mr Carrington? There's plenty to eat and drink.'

'I'm afraid it's impossible,' he apologised, 'but please accept the case of champagne I shall have sent in to you.' His glance returned to Samantha and, for a brief moment, she was conscious of his eyes looking keenly into her own. 'Perhaps we shall meet again, Miss Little. Goodnight.'

He turned on his heel then and left, taking something vital with him that made it impossible for Samantha to enjoy the rest of the evening. Clive, too, remained strangely reticent throughout the rest of the evening, but her encounter with Brett Carrington led to their first serious argument as he drove her home later that evening.

'What the devil were you doing with Brett Carrington?' he demanded, not taking his eyes off the road.

'I told you—I went for a walk and ended up in his private garden,' she explained once more. 'He found me there, we talked a bit, and then he offered me something to drink before he returned me to the party.' She glanced at Clive surreptitiously. 'I didn't know you were acquainted with Brett Carrington?'

Clive parked the car at the entrance to the flats and lit a cigarette, his hands shaking slightly. 'Well, if you must know, he and I had a bit of an argument some years ago and it wasn't very pleasant. I had hoped I would never have to meet him again, and it was absolute rotten luck that it had to be his garden you strolled into.' He drew hard on his cigarette and blew the smoke forcibly through the open window. 'What on earth made you go in there?'

'I don't know. I wasn't thinking, I suppose, and the garden looked so tempting and so very peaceful.' She felt her irritation rising swiftly. 'Really, Clive, you can't blame me for your embarrassment.'

'What did he say to you?'

'There in the garden, you mean?'

'Of course,' he snapped angrily, 'unless you'd rather not tell me the intimate details.'

'Oh, for goodness' sake, Clive, what was there for him to say?' she demanded hotly, her breath coming fast as she recalled her fright when he had emerged from the shadows to confront her. 'He was polite enough not to order me drastically off the premises and when he discovered that I'd strayed from the party, he offered to walk me back. What else was there for him to say or do?'

'You looked rather flushed,' he explained, glancing at her suspiciously. 'He didn't try anything, did he?'

Samantha stared at him aghast, the street light filtering dimly into the car so that she could see his angry, questioning expression without difficulty. 'Clive Wilmot, if you're suggesting that someone as wealthy and influential as Brett Carrington would consider cuddling a strange girl in a shadowy garden, then forget it. He's not the type.'

Clive relaxed then, flicking his cigarette out of the window before drawing her unresistingly into his arms. 'You're right, Sam. He's virtuous, pompous, and arrogant. Oh, hell, darling, let's forget it.'

Samantha was about to protest that he had started the discussion, but his lips got in the way and successfully swept aside all further thought of Brett Carrington and their brief encounter. As usual, Clive's kisses became possessive and demanding and, for the first time, Samantha felt strangely repulsed by his lack of control. She was not ready for the kind of relationship he desired and she had told him so earlier that evening. That sort of thing had to wait until after their marriage. Although she had fallen in love with him almost from the first moment they had met a month ago and found it a pleasurable sensation to know that he wanted her to such an extent, she could not tear down principles which had been erected since childhood. Because of this he appeared to become obsessed with possessing her.

'When will I see you again?' Clive murmured against her throat.

'Tomorrow evening, if you like,' she whispered, successfully avoiding his lips. 'I must go now.'

'I'll call for you at seven,' he announced, satisfied, yet still reluctant to release her.

It was Samantha who finally managed to struggle free of his warm embrace and slip from the car. It was, in a sense, becoming increasingly difficult to part from him and she longed for the day when there would be no need for him to leave her on the doorstep; a time when they could return to their own home where they could be together.

She was tiptoeing into the flat she shared with her father when she heard him call: 'Samantha, is that you?'

'Yes, Daddy. Did I wake you?'

'No, I couldn't sleep, so I thought a glass of warm milk might help,' he explained, emerging from the small kitchen in his pyjamas and dressing-gown.

Samantha, small, petite and fair, lived up to her name, whereas James Little was anything but small. Tall, lean and with dark hair flecked abundantly with grey, he was not at all what his name suggested. Samantha was more like her mother who had died so suddenly and unexpectedly from some unknown virus a year ago.

'Why is it that every time Clive and I go out somewhere, you suffer from insomnia?' she asked her father exasperatedly as she joined him in the kitchen. 'Why don't you like Clive? He's so nice.'

James Little frowned down into the glass of milk

before him on the table. 'That's the trouble, my dear, he's too nice to be true.'

'Oh, Daddy, stop being so suspicious!'

'I'm sorry, Samantha,' he apologised swiftly. 'I know you imagine yourself in love with him and that he's vaguely hinted at marriage, but I can't help feeling that his sincerity is nothing more than a bluff. He's stringing you along, my girl, and you've fallen for his charm because you're basically sweet and innocent.'

Samantha sprang instantly to the defence. 'Clive wants to marry me, but at the moment his salary is far from sufficient to——'

'If he earned a hundred thousand Rand a month,' her father interrupted cynically, 'his salary would still be insufficient. There'll always be another reason for not naming the day.'

There were few subjects on which she and her father disagreed, but Clive was one of them. On occasions such as this her anger rose sharply and she found it impossible to understand her father's reasoning. Clive had been nothing but polite and charming to her father on the rare occasions they had met, but her father persisted with this peculiar idea that Clive was anything but sincere.

'How can you say such things about him, Daddy!' she demanded, hurt and angry as she pulled out a chair and joined him at the table.

'I can say it, Samantha, because I'm a good deal older than you, and in my job as personnel manager I've met all types of people. Clive Wilmot is a bounder, and you're too blind to see it.'

Samantha slammed her fist on to the table. 'You have no right to say that! You don't know Clive as I do, and your opinion is biased. He loves me and wants to marry me—he's said so and I believe him.'

'Well, I hope for your sake that your faith is justified.' James Little mellowed slightly. 'You may be twenty, Samantha, but you're still my little girl, and I worry about you. I want you to be happy, but ... forgive me ... I can't see Clive Wilmot bringing you anything but sorrow.'

Samantha expelled the air from her lungs and knew that she was fighting a losing battle. 'Oh, Daddy, perhaps if you knew him better ...'

'Perhaps,' he agreed, although she could see from his expression that nothing would ever dissuade him from the opinion he had formed. He smiled at her suddenly and the tension evaporated. 'There's plenty of milk in the fridge. Make yourself some cocoa.'

'By the way, I met Brett Carrington quite by accident this evening at the Trydon Hotel,' she informed her father as she warmed the milk and searched for the jar of cocoa in the cupboard. 'You have heard of him, haven't you?'

'The name Carrington can open almost any door in the Eastern Cape, especially here in Port Elizabeth,' her father replied unexpectedly. 'How did you meet him?'

Samantha told him briefly of how she had wandered accidentally into Brett Carrington's private garden, and of the embarrassing moment when she was discovered and was told whom she was speaking to. But she carefully omitted the fact that Clive had been so upset at meeting an old acquaintance.

'Do you know him at all?' she asked casually as she mixed her cocoa and joined her father at the table once more. She could find no explanation for her unreasonable curiosity concerning a man she had met only briefly and she blushed under her father's direct scrutiny.

'I've heard a lot about him, you know how people talk, but I've never had the pleasure of meeting him.'

Samantha fingered her mug thoughtfully. 'I wonder what kind of man he really is.'

'From what I can gather he's thirty-eight and a confirmed bachelor. There are plenty of disillusioned mothers in the city who'd hoped to snare him as a son-in-law, but to date he's managed to evade them all successfully.' James Little chuckled slightly at his own remark before a sobering thought crossed his mind. 'His only sister died tragically a number of years ago. Rumour had it that she committed suicide, but no one seemed to know what actually happened, and Carrington has always been reluctant to discuss the subject.'

Samantha's curiosity deepened. 'How did the accident occur?'

Her father raised his dark eyebrows and shrugged as he emptied his glass of milk. 'She was ostensibly on her way to Port Elizabeth when her small sports car crashed through the rails on the Olifantskop Pass and plummeted down the mountain. Brett Carrington was with the rescue team that eventually went down with a helicopter to extract her body from the wreckage. It wasn't a pretty sight, by all accounts.'

Samantha's heart instantly stirred with pity. 'How terrible for him!'

A mischievous gleam entered her father's grey eyes. 'You appear to have an unusual interest in Brett Carrington,' he remarked teasingly, and had the satisfaction of seeing the colour deepening in her cheeks.

'I'm just curious,' she argued defensively. 'Someone like Brett Carrington always gives one the impression of being so self-sufficient and untouched by sorrow and strife that one tends to forget that they're only human after all.' She drained her mug of cocoa, in a hurry now to escape her father's prying eyes. 'I'm going to bed. Goodnight, Daddy.'

She kissed him swiftly and escaped to her room, but

it was a long time before she managed to fall asleep.
Her thoughts were filled with Clive's strange behaviour
at the sight of Brett Carrington, and the surprising information which her father had given her. She could
remember only too vividly the touch of his hand on
her elbow and those unusual eyes gazing down at her so
intently, adding to the confusion in her mind. What
kind of man was he? she wondered again, and it was
then that an alarming thought struck her. Brett Carrington was on the board of directors of the engineer-
ing firm she worked for. She realised now why his name
had rung a warning bell in her mind. The possibility
that they would meet again was not so great, but he had
stepped into her life as swiftly as he had emerged from
the shadows of the garden, and for some inexplicable
reason she had a premonition that he would be a disrupting influence in her relationship with Clive.

Gillian cornered Samantha at work the following
morning and could talk of nothing else but Samantha's
meeting with Brett Carrington.

'I always wondered what he actually looked like.
Newspaper photographs can be so deceptive.' She rolled
her eyes towards the ceiling and sighed ecstatically. 'If
I didn't love Stan so much, I could go for Brett Carrington in a big way!'

Samantha laughed outright, remembering how desperately in love Gillian had been with Stan before he
so much as noticed her. Gillian Forbes, red-haired and
green-eyed, had been her closest friend since they were
at high school together and, whereas Samantha was always the serious one, Gillian had always been the madcap daredevil, and being an adult had not changed her.

'You'd better not let Stan hear you,' Samantha reprimanded with a swift glance over her shoulder to the

glass partition surrounding Stan's office.

'Stan Dreyer had me chewing my nails long enough,' Gillian insisted, her eyes dancing with humour. 'It's time now that he suffered a few anxious moments. Who knows, he might appreciate me more.'

'You're not serious?' Samantha remarked hesitantly, knowing full well that her friend would quite easily do exactly as she had said.

'My dear Samantha,' Gillian said dramatically, 'Stan just had to smile at me and I fell into his lap like a ripe plum. Did he suffer at all during the lonely evenings and frustrating days when he had eyes for everyone else but me?' She shook her head adamantly. 'Oh, no! Stan had it all too easy.'

Samantha frowned slightly. 'You're not going to do anything irresponsible, are you?'

'Nothing irresponsible, darling, I promise you,' Gillian laughed mischievously, 'but I intend giving him quite a few anxious moments before the day I walk up that aisle to marry him. I'm going to look at and admire every other male in sight. He mustn't get the idea that he was the only fish in the sea.'

'Poor Stan,' Samantha sympathised as she visualised what Gillian had in mind. 'Don't forget in the process that he loves you very much.'

'I shan't forget either how much I love *him*,' Gillian laughed happily.

Samantha glanced ruefully at the pile of work mounting up on her desk, but Gillian evidently had no intention of leaving yet.

'What was up with Clive last night?' she asked.

'Clive?' Samantha asked innocently.

'Don't hedge,' Gillian remarked urgently. 'He went absolutely white when he saw you walking in with Brett Carrington, and I don't think that he quite recovered from the shock during the rest of the evening.'

'It was nothing really,' Samantha replied evasively. Like her father, Gillian was not over-fond of Clive and made no effort to hide the fact that she did not approve of Samantha's choice. 'They just don't get on very well,' she added lamely. 'Mr Carrington and Clive, I mean.'

'I'll bet they don't,' her friend remarked scathingly. 'Brett Carrington isn't a fool, and Clive is so transparent——'

'Gillian, please,' Samantha begged, and her friend was instantly contrite as she saw the look of pain flash briefly across Samantha's sensitive features.

'I'm sorry, Sam,' she said softly, her hand gripping Samantha's shoulder. 'I didn't mean to hurt you, but I wish you hadn't fallen in love with Clive Wilmot. He wasn't meant for you, I just know it!'

Samantha managed a weary smile. 'My father will certainly agree with you, but I wish you'd both give Clive a chance to prove himself without condemning him outright.'

'Sam, I must admit he's suave and charming, and devilishly attractive in a lean sort of way with that fair hair of his and his handsome boyish features,' Gillian sighed despairingly, 'but I can't help the feeling I get that under all that marvellous exterior there lurks something quite unpleasant.'

'You're biased, like my father.'

'Perhaps,' Gillian agreed, ignoring the danger signals in Samantha's usually soft blue eyes. 'I just hope you won't be disillusioned. I would hate to see you badly hurt.'

'I shan't be,' Samantha insisted stubbornly, but Gillian merely shrugged her shoulders characteristically as she walked across to her own desk.

There was fortunately no time for Samantha to

brood over their conversation as she steadily worked her way through the amount of typing in her basket. She snatched a cup of tea at ten that morning and then set to work once more without delay. At lunch time the pile had diminished considerably and it was with a feeling of relief that she went down to the cafeteria to have something to eat.

Gillian had rushed into town with Stan to do a bit of shopping, so Samantha found herself without her friend's usual bright company, but for once, she was glad to be alone.

Dear Gillian! she thought amusedly. Like her father, Gillian meant well, yet they were both so absurd to doubt Clive's intentions.

CHAPTER TWO

SAMANTHA was pouring her tea after a light lunch when she had the most peculiar sensation that someone was observing her closely from across the room. She turned her head slightly and her startled glance locked with that of Brett Carrington. Her breath caught in her throat as he inclined his head towards her before excusing himself from his companion and threading his way among the crowded tables towards her. What could he possibly want with her? she wondered frantically as she observed with almost hypnotic fascination the panther-like quality in his walk as he approached her purposefully.

'Escape now,' something warned her, but it was a futile instruction, for her limbs were too numb to obey.

'May I join you?'

'Please do,' Samantha murmured, colouring slightly and conscious of the fact that heads were turning in their direction as Brett Carrington pulled out a chair and sat down. 'There's still enough tea in the pot. Could I fetch another cup, Mr Carrington?'

'No, thank you, I've just had tea.' His keen glance swept over her, taking in the neat grey skirt and crisp white blouse. 'I had no idea you worked here.'

'You never asked for my credentials when I so rudely invaded your privacy last night,' she replied lightly.

'I'm shattered at my own neglect,' he mocked her. 'However, fortune has smiled on me once again it seems.'

Samantha's dark blue eyes were questioning. 'I don't think I understand.'

'Don't you?' His mouth was firm, with a hint of sensuality in the lower lip as it relaxed into a smile. 'It doesn't matter. I hope the rest of your evening was enjoyable?'

'It was ... pleasant, thank you.'

If he was aware of the slight hesitation and her utter confusion at his presence then he showed no sign of it.

'How long have you known Clive Wilmot?'

It was an unexpected and direct question that immediately put her on the defensive. 'Mr Carrington, I fail to see that it's any business of yours.'

Brett Carrington's angular face hardened. 'I was merely making polite conversation, Miss Little, and not prying into your affairs.'

'I'm sorry, I didn't mean to be rude. It's just that ...' She bit her lip nervously, angry with herself for allowing a simple question to rattle her, and realising that she owed this man some sort of explanation for her rudeness, she said: 'Clive Wilmot has become a rather touchy subject lately with my father and my closest friend, Gillian. You met her last night,' she ended lamely.

'Am I to understand that they don't entirely approve of your friendship with Wilmot?'

'No, they don't.'

'Perhaps they have reason?'

Samantha's unreasonable anger and irritation grew swiftly. 'Oh, please, not you as well, Mr Carrington!'

'May I ask you again how long you've known him?'

She looked up into his dark brown eyes and knew she could not evade his direct question on this occasion. 'Just over a month.'

'I see.'

'What do you see, Mr Carrington?' she asked abruptly, noticing the cynical twist to his lips.

'It takes years to get to know some people, yet with others it can take no longer than five minutes.'

'What are you insinuating?'

There was a gleam of amusement in his eyes that puzzled her. 'I'm not insinuating anything. I'm merely trying to point out that some people are transparent, where others are inclined to hide behind a mask.'

'Aren't we all inclined to wear a mask where others are concerned?' she asked hotly, no longer caring that this elegantly dressed man in his dark brown suit could quite easily see to it that she lost her job. 'Don't *you*, Mr Carrington?'

Those strong, well-shaped hands gestured expressively. 'There are times when it's necessary, I agree, but it depends on the people you're with.'

'Exactly,' Samantha replied with satisfaction. She had proved her point with Brett Carrington, she thought with an unusual sense of elation.

'I shan't argue with you, Miss Little, but may I ask you to render me a small service before I leave you?'

He had risen to his feet and heads turned swiftly in their direction once more as he towered over her.

'If I can help you, I . . . I will,' she replied with uncertainty.

'Could you give me Clive Wilmot's business address?'

Relieved that it was no more than that, she gave him the address without so much as a twinge of curiosity and watched him write it down in a small notebook which he replaced immediately in his jacket pocket. There was an unmistakable hint of mockery in his eyes as he glanced down at her once more.

'We shall meet again, Samantha Little,' he said. 'I would very much like to continue our interesting discussion.'

Samantha stared after him until he was out of sight with an uncomfortable feeling that she had been beaten after all. Brett Carrington, she sensed, was not a man to be thwarted, and neither was he a fool. When he wanted something, he would go out of his way to get it, and, with this thought, Samantha felt strangely trapped.

Two days later life was entirely disrupted by an unexpected telephone call from Clive.

'Sam darling, I'm afraid I have to cancel our plans for this evening,' he told her ruefully. 'The firm is sending me to the Cape Town branch to relieve the chap there for three weeks. That means I shan't be back until the middle of February.'

'Oh, no!' she moaned, distraught with disappointment. 'Will I see you before you go?'

'I'm afraid not, darling,' he dashed her hopes. 'I'm leaving on the six-thirty flight this evening.'

'I could borrow Daddy's car and drive out to the airport,' she suggested desperately. 'I might just make it in time.'

'Sam darling, that would be splendid,' he exclaimed, sounding more cheerful while her heart twisted within her.

'I hate the thought of not seeing you for three whole weeks,' she sighed.

'It's damnable, I know, but what could I do?'

'Nothing, Clive,' she told him dismally, 'except to go and hurry back as soon as your time there is up.'

Clive's soft laugh came across the wires and her heart quickened. 'Have I ever told you that you're a marvellously unselfish and understanding person, Sam?'

'I'm not really, Clive,' she protested, close to tears, 'but thanks for the compliment anyway.'

'I'll see you later, then. Cheerio for now, my love.'

The line went dead and Samantha replaced the receiver with an acute sense of dread. Three weeks without Clive! It was going to feel like an eternity with nothing to look forward to in the evenings except hours of longing.

'Bad news, Sam?' Gillian asked, pushing her work aside and turning to her friend.

'Clive is going away for three weeks,' she said dully.

'Oh?'

Samantha explained swiftly, adding: 'I shall miss him terribly.'

'Cheer up, Sam, it isn't as if he'll be gone for ever, you know.'

'You're right, Gillian,' Samantha replied, making an effort to control her dismal thoughts. 'What's three weeks compared with a whole lifetime we shall spend together?'

'Exactly,' Gillian remarked emphatically. She changed the subject instantly and Samantha was grateful to her friend for trying to take her mind off her present unhappiness. But, despite Gillian's efforts, the immediate future looked bleak and empty without Clive.

Samantha took her usual bus home that evening and lingered only long enough to explain to her father that she would be returning a little later. She drove to the airport as fast as the speed limit through Walmer would allow and arrived there only minutes before Clive's flight was called.

'Sam darling!' he cried as he saw her enter the building. 'I was afraid you might not make it.'

She flung herself unashamedly into his outstretched arms. 'Nearly all the traffic lights caught me. I was absolutely frantic!'

'All that matters is that you're here, my sweet,' Clive

told her seriously, kissing her waiting lips with a warmth that quickened her heart. Moments later his flight to Cape Town was called and he glanced at her regretfully. 'I must go, my pet.'

'Oh, Clive, I shall miss you!' she cried, unexpected tears brimming her eyes.

'And I shall miss you too, darling,' he replied, drawing her into his warm embrace as he kissed her for the last time before hastening towards the departure gate.

Samantha saw him go through a film of tears and remained where she was until the Boeing had soared into the swiftly darkening sky. For a moment she felt frightened and desperately alone before she shook herself mentally and told herself not to be silly. Clive *would* be returning and, if she kept herself busy, the time would pass quickly.

She went to work the following day, determined not to let Clive's absence upset her more than necessary, but half-way through the morning something happened that made her wish she had boarded that plane with him. The telephone on Gillian's desk rang shrilly and, after answering it, she placed the receiver beside the telephone.

'You're wanted on the phone, Sam.'

Mystified, Samantha went across to her desk and lifted the receiver, placing her hand over the mouthpiece. 'Who is it?'

Gillian shrugged. 'It's an internal call. The voice sounds familiar, but I just can't place him at the moment.'

'Who could it be?' Samantha questioned, frowning down at her anxiously.

'You won't find out that way,' Gillian remarked, grinning mischievously as she gestured towards the receiver. 'Talk to the man and find out what he wants, or I shall burst with curiosity!'

A warning flashed through Samantha's mind, but with a curiosity to match Gillian's she raised the receiver to her ear. 'Samantha Little speaking.'

'Ah, I was beginning to think you couldn't be found,' a deep voice said abruptly.

Samantha's nerves were instantly electrified. 'Mr Carrington!'

'Were you expecting a call from someone else?' he queried mockingly, his voice vibrating across the line.

'N-No,' she stammered foolishly, clutching at the desk. 'What can I do for you?'

'I was wondering if I might persuade you to have dinner with me this evening.'

She sagged against Gillian's desk and stared into her friend's questioning eyes. 'I—I'm afraid I can't. C-Clive is taking me out this evening,' she lied, grabbing at the only straw she possessed for safety. But safety from what? she wondered confusedly.

Gillian smothered a giggle behind her hand just as Brett Carrington's easy tones rang in Samantha's ear. 'Can't you think of a better excuse?'

'What do you mean?'

'I happen to know that Clive Wilmot will be out of town for the next three weeks. I am right, am I not?'

She was trapped, she realised with heavily thudding heart and flaming cheeks. 'Who—who told you this?'

'You could say I have my ear to the ground,' he replied mockingly. 'Will you have dinner with me this evening, and allow me to entertain you in his absence?'

'I—I couldn't. I——'

'I'll call for you at seven and we can have dinner at my hotel,' he interrupted, taking no notice of her stammered protests and precipitating her next excuse.

'There's no need to dress, it will be quite informal.'

'But I haven't said——'

'But you will,' he interrupted with an infuriating confidence that took her breath away.

'Yes,' she heard herself accepting as if she were listening to someone else.

'Seven o'clock?'

'Yes,' she agreed mechanically.

'Good,' his voice came abruptly over the line. 'I look forward to seeing you, Samantha.'

The line went dead and Samantha stared incredulously at the lifeless instrument in her hand.

'What did the great Brett Carrington want?' she heard Gillian ask as she dropped the receiver on to its hood with an angry gesture.

'He's invited me to have dinner with him this evening.' It sounded even more incredible speaking those words aloud and she felt quite dazed just thinking about it.

Gillian's eyes widened considerably. 'Well, well, well!'

'Don't say it like that!'

'Darling Sam,' Gillian laughed up into her friend's apprehensive blue eyes. 'Don't you realise what an honour it is to be asked to dine with a man like Brett Carrington? There are girls in this city who would give their false eyelashes for an invitation like that!'

'I know, I know, but ...' She swallowed violently, struggling to regain her composure before she met Gillian's glance with panic-stricken eyes. 'Gillian, I'm frightened!'

'For heaven's sake, Sam,' Gillian laughed reassuringly, drawing a chair closer and pushing Samantha into it. 'He can't eat you, and it isn't as if he has a reputation with women.'

Samantha smiled. 'I'm not afraid he might try to seduce me, if that's what you mean. And I'm not bluffing myself that he has any lasting interest in me. Besides, it would take an extraordinarily attractive woman to capture the heart of Brett Carrington.'

Gillian stared at her for several seconds with a gleam of tolerant amusement in her eyes. 'That's what I like most about you, Sam. You're always so unpretentious and so blessedly unaware of the fact that you're one of the most beautiful girls I've ever clapped eyes on.'

'You're a good friend, Gillian, but you do tend to exaggerate at times.'

'Don't underestimate yourself, darling,' Gillian continued unperturbed. 'Brett Carrington may have no interest in marriage to the local opposite sex, but I have yet to meet a man who doesn't appreciate beauty when he sees it.'

'I'm not interested in Brett Carrington's opinion of my appearance,' Samantha protested irritably. 'Oh, if only Clive were here!'

'But he isn't, so why not allow Brett Carrington to take your mind off Clive for a while? There can be no harm in that, surely?'

'But I don't want anyone or anything to take my mind off Clive,' Samantha cried, curling her small hands into fists. 'I love him!'

'More's the pity,' she heard Gillian mutter, but she was too disturbed at the thought of dining with Brett Carrington that evening to take offence. 'Just make up your mind that you're going to enjoy yourself this evening, and you will,' Gillian added with confidence.

Samantha returned to her own desk and wished five o'clock would never come. She thought strongly about pretending to be ill, but knew somehow that Brett Carrington would not let the matter rest there. Perhaps the only solution would be to get the evening over and done with, she decided unhappily, but she would make it quite clear to him that after this evening she would not be available for further invitations.

James Little appeared rather doubtful when Samantha told him about the unexpected invitation she had received. If he had thought that she was merely pulling his leg, then he was forced to believe her when he found himself sitting down to a solitary meal while Samantha bathed and changed into a semi-evening dress that matched the colour of her eyes superbly. With a billowing skirt and halter-neck top it was not too formal and cool enough for that warm summer evening. Without intending to, she had taken more than the usual care when dressing that evening, and her pale gold hair shone like a halo after she had brushed it vigorously away from her face to fall softly on her neck.

When she finally entered the lounge where her father was reading the evening paper, he glanced up and whistled appreciatively, but she found it difficult to hide the nervousness that seemed to twist her stomach into a permanent knot.

'If you would rather not go I'll make some excuse, Samantha,' he offered generously, but Samantha shook her head firmly.

'It'll be no use, Daddy. Brett Carrington isn't the kind of man to be fobbed off with excuses. I tried and failed.'

Her father folded the newspaper carefully and dropped it on the floor beside his chair to give her his undivided attention. 'I don't suppose it's occurred to you that you might enjoy his company?'

'I doubt it,' she remarked, firmly convinced that the evening was going to be a disaster from beginning to end.

At seven o'clock precisely the doorbell chimed and

Samantha turned frightened eyes towards her father.

'Brett Carrington is obviously a very punctual man,' James remarked calmly, and she laughed nervously as she rose to her feet.

'If he's punctual, then I don't suppose he would like to be kept waiting,' she tried to be flippant as she left the lounge. She closed her eyes for a moment, fighting to control her quivering nerves before she lifted the latch and opened the door.

'Good evening, Samantha,' Brett Carrington smiled down at her from his great height, and she could not help but admire his splendid physique which was clad in immaculate grey trousers, matching grey tweed jacket, and a silk scarf tucked into the neck of his white shirt.

'Won't—won't you come in?' she stammered, aware that she had been staring and furious with herself when she noticed the gleam of amusement in his dark eyes.

He followed her into the lounge and, to her surprise, some of the tension left her when, after making the necessary introductions, she discovered that there was an instant rapport between the two men. She could do nothing but stare as she saw Brett Carrington and her father, completely relaxed and at ease in each other's company, chatting as though they were old acquaintances. If only Clive and her father could get on in this way, she thought with a stab of pain.

Perhaps this was where the fault lay in the relationship between Clive and her father, she thought ten minutes later as she sat stiffly beside Brett Carrington in his silver Jaguar. Clive seldom took the trouble to talk to her father and, when he did, it always appeared as though he was in a hurry to get away. He never really gave her father the opportunity to get to know him, or endeavoured to spend time with him as Brett had done.

It was an awkward situation she felt incapable of rectifying.

'You look exceptionally lovely this evening, Samantha Little,' Brett Carrington interrupted her thoughts. He placed a hand over hers where she gripped them nervously in her lap. 'I would prefer it, though, if you were more relaxed and not so silent.'

'I—I'm sorry.' Those warm, strong fingers sent an electrifying current along her ragged nerves and she was forced to clamp her teeth together for a moment to stop their chattering. 'I didn't w-want to come with you, you know that.'

He released her hands instantly and a tense silence hung between them. She was just beginning to think that she had mortally offended him when she heard him chuckle softly to himself.

'You're refreshingly honest, and I like that,' he explained as she glanced at him questioningly. 'Perhaps a good wine and excellently prepared food will alter your disposition.'

Samantha was not sure what she had expected, but she had certainly not bargained with going up to the third floor in his private lift to his elegantly and expensively furnished suite where a dinner for two had been laid out on a small table at a window overlooking the sea. Soft lights and subdued music added to the atmosphere while white-clad waiters discreetly served the most exquisite meal she had ever tasted and left them ostentatiously alone to enjoy it.

Samantha could not recall at what stage during the meal she began to lose some of the tension within her, but she never ceased to be wary of the man seated opposite her. She was aware of him in every fibre of her being, and it was an awareness that frightened her and placed her involuntarily on her guard.

'How did you know where I lived?' she asked curiously, recalling suddenly that he had not asked for her address when he had issued his unexpected invitation to have dinner with him.

Their coffee had been poured in small coffee cups of the most delicate china and Brett Carrington gestured to the waiter that they would help themselves to more coffee if they so desired.

'You've perhaps forgotten,' he began when they were alone once more, 'that I have access to the staff files?'

'Of course.' How foolish of her not to have realised this. No one would have thought it strange for one of the directors to ask for an employee's file which he could scrutinise at leisure. The nervousness which had lain dormant almost throughout the entire meal reared itself once more, and knowing that she was dining with one of the most sought-after men in the Eastern Cape only served to heighten her discomfort.

Brett Carrington offered her a cigarette from a slim gold case and, when she refused, he lit one for himself and leaned back in his chair, his eyes narrowed as he glanced at her through a film of smoke.

'I discovered also that after you left school you attended a secretarial college for a year before joining this firm. Eighteen months ago you were promoted to private secretary to the Assistant General Manager, but after a week you requested a transfer back to your old job.' His glance was intense and inscrutable. 'Why?'

Samantha's heartbeats quickened as she lowered her glance. 'My reasons were of a personal nature.'

'I could make it my business to find out.'

Her troubled blue gaze was pleading. 'I don't wish to discuss it.'

Brett Carrington's mouth tightened. 'Did the A.G.M. demand more than your secretarial services from you?'

Samantha felt the blood rush to her face as she stared at him incredulously. 'You know?'

'Everyone knows that his secretaries are specially chosen for that purpose,' he replied bluntly, crushing his half-smoked cigarette into the silver ashtray. 'There are girls who relish such jobs, but you obviously do not, or you wouldn't blush just talking about it.'

She could not bear the scrutiny of his dark eyes and lowered her glance. 'I've never discussed the subject with anyone before.'

'It's understandable,' she heard him say drily. 'I've discovered quite a lot about you, Samantha Little, in a short space of time. Perhaps you might care to fill in the missing pieces to the puzzle?'

Samantha felt her hands trembling in her lap as she glanced at him suspiciously. 'Is that why you invited me to have dinner with you?'

'Would it shock you to know that for some reason you interest me a great deal, Samantha?'

She considered this in silence for a moment before replying, 'It doesn't shock me, Mr Carrington, but——'

'Brett,' he interrupted swiftly. 'My friends call me Brett.' He smiled briefly at her discomfort. 'You were saying?'

'I fail to see why I should interest you.'

There was an unmistakable gleam of mockery in his eyes that did nothing for her confidence. 'Does there have to be a reason?'

'There usually is, when a man like yourself becomes interested in an ordinary girl like myself.'

'Are you in love with Clive Wilmot?'

The question was so sudden that for a moment Samantha stared at him blankly. 'Really! I don't see——'

'That it's any business of mine,' he finished for her

with a hint of impatience. 'Would you prefer it if I questioned others about your personal life?'

She stared at him aghast, floundering hopelessly but, as he was about to refill her glass, she begged: 'Oh, please, no more wine.'

'Come, Samantha, have some more and relax,' he coaxed and, without waiting for a reply, he replenished her glass. 'I don't intend to eat you,' he echoed Gillian's remark, topping up his own glass before glancing questioningly at her, his heavy eyebrows raised autocratically. 'Well, do I get a reply to my question?'

'If you must know ... yes, I am in love with him.'

'Has he asked you to marry him yet?'

Samantha shifted uncomfortably in her chair. 'Not in so many words, but we've discussed marriage.'

Why on earth was she allowing him to drag all this information from her? she wondered angrily. It was none of his business, yet it was impossible not to answer his probing questions. He had her over a barrel and he knew it. Damn him!

'Do you think he *will* ask you to marry him?'

Despite her valiant efforts, her anger rose sharply. 'I fail to see why I should continue answering questions which have absolutely nothing to do with you. Your prying has gone far enough, Mr Carrington!'

One strong brown hand closed firmly over hers where it lay clenched on the table between them, and Samantha blinked her eyes in surprise as she stared at it.

'I would hate to think of someone as beautiful as yourself being hoodwinked, Samantha. I would also hate to see your innocence marred.'

His voice was warm and vibrant, and strangely sincere, yet she could not heed his obvious warning. She trusted Clive and she had to believe that he loved her as much she she loved him. Dear, darling Clive, who was not there at that moment to defend himself.

'Clive would never do anything to hurt me.'

'Famous last words,' Brett observed easily, 'if you'll forgive the old cliché.'

She averted her glance, staring instead through the open window to where the calm sea lay shimmering in the moonlight, depicting a peace and serenity she was far from experiencing. She had always been able to trust her own judgment in the past, so why should she not trust it where Clive was concerned? Why was everyone so bent upon destroying their relationship? Why did they find it so difficult to believe that Clive was sincere? Was Brett Carrington's cynicism perhaps as a result of the argument that had taken place between himself and Clive? Surely not! Brett did not appear to be the kind of man who would bear a grudge and then deliberately set out to destroy someone else's happiness.

When he drove her home that evening, she made up her mind that she would avoid him at all costs in future, if only for her own peace of mind.

'What is it that you have against Clive?' she asked bluntly as he took the key from her and unlocked the door to the flat. 'Why have you been trying your best to make me believe he's a scoundrel of some sort?'

His eyebrows rose sharply. 'My dear Samantha, I've done nothing of the kind. I'm merely trying to place you on your guard against the pitfalls of life. I can sense that you're much too trusting, and absolutely sincere in everything you do, but that doesn't mean that others share your admirable principles.'

Samantha stared at him for several seconds in the dimly lit entrance to the flat, but his expression remained formidable.

'I'm sorry I mentioned this subject once more,' she

said dully. 'I don't really wish to continue this discussion further.'

'Right, let's change the subject,' he agreed. 'What are you doing tomorrow evening?'

Samantha held her breath. 'Why?'

'I have two tickets for a show in town and we could have dinner afterwards.'

'Thank you very much for the invitation, but——'

'That's settled, then,' he interrupted her refusal, and she leaned weakly against the door in an effort to control the unfamiliar weakness in her knees.

'Mr Carrington, I——'

'Brett,' he corrected, leaning closer to her, and for one wild moment she thought he was going to kiss her. Panic held her in its fierce grip as she stared into his rugged face so close to hers. His glance swept over her upturned face and lingered for a moment on her trembling lips before he straightened and twisted his lips into a mocking smile. 'You've avoided using my name all evening, but I insist that you use it now.'

'Brett,' she managed finally, not wishing to prolong the evening. 'I must thank you for your kind invitation just now, but the answer is . . . no.'

To her chagrin he smiled at her tolerantly as if she were an amusing child. 'Despite the fact that you say no very prettily, Samantha, I shall call for you at six-thirty tomorrow evening and hope that you've changed your mind.'

Without waiting for a reply he turned on his heel and disappeared down the stairs. Samantha stood as if she had been mesmerised until she heard the silver Jaguar drive away. Brett Carrington was really the most infuriating man she had ever met, she decided as she went inside and locked the door behind her. His arrogant refusal to accept no for an answer only made her more determined that, no matter what, she would not be ready and waiting for him when he arrived the following evening.

Later, as she lay staring into the darkness, she tried to think of Clive, but Brett Carrington's angular face kept intruding into her thoughts. Time and again she banished him until she finally gave up, allowing her mind to conjure up his image. The thick, almost black hair, greying at the temples, the dark brown eyes beneath heavy black eyebrows, with a straight nose and square chin. She thought again of how he had looked in that moment when she had feared that he would kiss her, and for one horrified moment she wondered what it would feel like to have that chiselled mouth pressed against her own.

Placing her hands against her hot cheeks, she felt an incredible anger rising within her. What was happening to her? How dared she entertain such thoughts about a man like Brett Carrington? The reason for his sudden interest in her was beyond her understanding, but she would not allow him to dominate her life in this way. Clive would be back within three weeks, and until then she would have to be on her guard against Brett. He had wealth and influence as well as being in a position of authority and, even at this early stage she had a feeling that, given the opportunity, he could wield a strange power over her, a power that could quite easily drive Clive from her heart and mind.

Brett Carrington was not a man to be overlooked, and her feminine instincts warned her that, like so many others before her, she could become an easy prey to a man of his experience.

'Oh, Clive,' she moaned softly to herself, 'why did you have to be sent away just at the time when I needed you most?' But would Clive be able to protect her adequately from something she was unable to explain even to herself?

She thumped her pillow and tried to sleep instead of allowing her thoughts to go round in endless circles that led nowhere in particular. Everything will make more sense in the morning, she consoled herself.

CHAPTER THREE

'WELL?' Gillian demanded the following morning at work. 'Was it as bad as you thought it would be?'

'No,' Samantha shook her head, 'but I would rather see as little as possible of Brett Carrington in future.'

'Don't tell me he made a pass at you!'

'Gillian,' Samantha replied with mock severity, 'a man like Brett Carrington doesn't make passes at a girl.'

'No, I don't suppose he would,' Gillian nodded gravely, adding with a hint of humour, 'I must admit Stan and I were hoping he would sweep you off your feet.'

Samantha laughed outright at her friend's admission. 'I never gave him the opportunity, and he behaved like a perfect gentleman all evening.'

'How disappointing,' Gillian murmured half in earnest. 'I had hoped he would at least make you realise that there were far more interesting men about for a girl to fall in love with.'

'Gillian,' Samantha reprimanded, 'I happen to be in love with Clive, and as far as Brett Carrington is concerned ... well, I want no part of him.'

'What a pity, because he has all the qualities most women admire. He had a wonderful physique and such good vibrations, and added to that he's so terribly rich!'

'That may be so, but he doesn't interest me at all.'

'Where did you have dinner?' Gillian asked exasperatedly. 'At a restaurant in town?'

'No, in his private suite at the hotel.'

Gillian pouted her lips and whistled softly. 'Just as well Clive isn't here. Were you alone?'

'There was a bevy of servants who very discreetly managed to make us feel as though we were alone,' Samantha told her with a touch of irritation.

'Has he asked you to go out with him again?'

'Yes ... but I shall refuse to go,' Samantha added swiftly, determined that she would remain adamant about not seeing him again.

She should have realised, however, that Brett Carrington was a force to be reckoned with. He arrived at the flat that evening at six-thirty sharp and found her dressed in a pair of old slacks and sweater, and sitting cross-legged on the lounge carpet with several dress patterns and pieces of material in disarray about her. Encouraged by her father, who thought the whole episode amusing, Brett instructed her to change immediately, glancing at his wristwatch and giving her not much more than ten minutes to do so.

Infuriated, she gathered up the patterns and material and escaped to her room, slamming the door behind her and locking it. He could wait there in the lounge for ever as far as she was concerned, she thought, but fear of what he might do when provoked made her change swiftly into something more appropriate. Brett Carrington was to have his way after all, she thought helplessly.

The show he had tickets for turned out to be a classic tragedy that left her on the verge of tears towards the end, and he mocked her gently throughout dinner about being tender-hearted, finally succeeding in making her wonder why she had been so afraid to accept his invitation in the first place.

Brett was pleasant company, but there was Clive to

consider. She had to remain faithful to him in every respect, but was there really any harm in accepting a few casual invitations from one of the directors of the firm she worked for? Samantha knew somehow that she was merely making excuses for herself when every nerve in her body was crying out that she should take care. She had hoped that Clive would have telephoned her soon after his arrival in Cape Town, but after two days had passed without a word from him she felt somehow justified in allowing Brett Carrington to monopolise her free time to such an extent, but that was all!

Samantha was quite mollified that evening when Brett left her on the doorstep without so much as a peck on the cheek. His behaviour that evening had been impeccable, just as it had been the evening before, and Samantha began to wonder whether she had allowed her imagination to run away with her. She would not see him again, she was sure. After issuing an invitation to her on two consecutive evenings in a row, he would now have tired of her company, she told herself happily.

She was mistaken, however, for Brett became a regular visitor at her home during the following two weeks. He would either invite her out to dinner or take her to a show, and quite often he would spend the evening sitting in one of their brightly covered armchairs, exchanging views with her father while she sat and stared in amazement at the way her father responded to their important visitor. 'Important' was rather a mild word to describe Brett, for his bearing and manner made it quite obvious that he was used to having his every command carried out promptly. He was also, she had to admit, someone who could be depended upon in every way, and a man who expected honesty in return for the same. It was perhaps these characteristics of his that had her father eating out of his hand in a short space of time.

'We don't see much of you these days, Sam,' Stan Dreyer remarked one morning when he joined Gillian and herself during their tea break in the cafeteria. 'I hear you're hobnobbing with the cream of society lately.'

'Don't be silly, Stan,' Samantha rebuked him good-humouredly. 'Once Clive has returned Brett Carrington will realise that I have no interest in him whatsoever, but until then why shouldn't I go on enjoying myself while Clive is away?'

'There's no reason at all why you shouldn't enjoy yourself,' Stan agreed readily. 'I'm sure Clive is——'

He broke off suddenly as Gillian rammed him in the ribs with her elbow and gave him a fierce look. Samantha could not help noticing this, but decided to ignore the implication that Clive would be anything but faithful to her. He had telephoned her only once during the two weeks he had been away, and it had been a very unsatisfactory call, for the line had been bad at the time, which made conversing intelligently impossible. She was able to understand, however, that he would not telephone again owing to pressure of work, but that he would contact her as soon as he returned from Cape Town. Samantha accepted this as gracefully as she could, because it would, after all, not be long before she saw him again. Hearing Clive's voice, however badly due to the disturbances on the line, had merely served to re-awaken her longing for him, and she began to count the days to his return.

Samantha arrived at work one morning to find Gillian and Brett Carrington deep in conversation on the steps leading to the entrance of the offices. Curious as to why her friend should be wearing such a serious expression, Samantha approached more swiftly, but Gillian saw her coming and gave a guilty start. Brett turned at that moment, his expression perfectly calm as he smiled down at her.

'Good morning, Samantha.'

She returned the greeting, her cheeks flaming for some unknown reason as his glance swept over her appreciatively from her pale gold hair to her soft leather shoes. Gillian added to her embarrassment by hastily excusing herself and entering the building, leaving Brett and herself alone on the steps. Samantha tried to follow suit, but found her arm held firmly above the elbow.

'Will you have lunch with me?'

'I have some typing to get through during lunch,' Samantha hedged, aware of the magnetism of this tall, immaculately dressed man who had fallen into step beside her.

'I know of a place nearby where the service is quick and the meals superb,' Brett persisted persuasively, and even without looking at him she knew there would be a gleam of mockery in his eyes because of her continual reluctance to accept his invitations.

'Why can't you take no for an answer?' she sighed, as they reached the door to the general office.

'Because you don't really mean it, Samantha,' he replied arrogantly. 'You can't deny that you've enjoyed my company these past two weeks, can you?'

Samantha shook her head helplessly. 'No, I can't deny it, but——'

'Then why do you continually want to deny me the pleasure of your company?'

'There's Clive,' she reminded him.

'Clive is almost eight hundred kilometres from Port Elizabeth at the moment, but I'm here,' he stated firmly. 'I shall be waiting for you at the front entrance. Twelve-thirty?'

An involuntary smile plucked at her lips as she nodded and pushed past him into the office. His manner was infuriating, his arrogance breathtaking, yet she could not deny that his company was stimulating and never dull.

Samantha never did find the time to ask Gillian the reason for her serious discussion with Brett but there was something in the way Gillian stared at her from time to time that disturbed her. At such times Gillian would switch instantly to her usual madcap self, and Samantha would eventually be left to wonder whether her imagination had played tricks on her. Whatever it was that they had discussed in such earnest, Gillian was obviously not going to tell her, and Samantha knew her friend too well to pry.

After that luncheon date with Brett she did not see him again until he arrived at the flat one evening, three days before Clive's return to Port Elizabeth. Samantha was shampooing her hair when the doorbell chimed and, thinking that her father might have forgotten his latch key and was returning for it, she rinsed her hair and wrapped a towel about her head before going to the door.

'Daddy isn't home this evening,' she said stupidly when she found herself confronted by Brett's tall, imposing figure. 'He's at a meeting.'

'I know,' Brett smiled, his glance flicking over her beige slacks and loose-fitting blouse as he closed the door behind him and followed her into the lounge.

Flustered by his unexpected appearance, she stood in the middle of the floor and wished the roof would cave in on her as he seated himself in the only comfortable armchair they possessed, behaving as though it was nothing unusual for him to see her with a towel wrapped like a turban about her head.

Her trembling hands were seized suddenly and she was pulled down on to her knees before him. It was so unexpected that she found no time for protest as she felt his hands undoing the towel.

'I used to dry my sister's hair for her,' he explained quietly at her questioning glance, and proceeded to rub her hair vigorously until her scalp tingled pleasurably.

It was a perfectly natural situation, yet somehow she had never associated Brett Carrington with the menial task of drying a woman's hair. Neither had she bargained for the unwanted though pleasurable sensations caused by his nearness. It was at a time like this that she had to force herself to remember that her heart belonged to Clive alone.

'I believe your sister died a few years ago,' she remarked, not particularly wanting to discuss a subject which might be painful to him, but it happened to be the first thing that came to mind when she felt the need to break the heavy silence between them.

Surprisingly enough he said quite casually: 'That's right. Who told you?'

'My father, but I believe he read it in the newspapers at the time.'

'Yes, it was a terrible waste of such a young life,' he stated firmly, letting the towel fall to the floor.

There was a touch of bitterness in the glance that met hers and then, realising that she must look a mess, she hastily excused herself. In the sanctuary of her room she quickly combed her hair, the feathery yet still damp curls refusing to remain in position and curling about her ears. Exasperated, she let them be and touched up her make-up before returning to the lounge.

Brett stood at the window with his back to her. He had removed his jacket and his shirt was spanning almost too tightly across the width of his shoulders. He turned to face her then, almost as if he had sensed her presence, and something quivered in her throat at the graveness of his expression.

'There's something I want to discuss with you,' he said brusquely, adding to her nervousness.

'Oh?'

The only other occasions when he had adopted this serious attitude was when they had discussed Clive, and Samantha prepared herself mentally to do battle with him as he came towards her and gripped her shoulders until she winced inwardly.

'Samantha, I want you to stop deluding yourself that Wilmot will ever marry you. He won't ... and when that happens I may not be around to pick up the pieces.'

'How dare you!' she exclaimed angrily, shaking off his hands.

'I dare because I happen to care what happens to you when you discover the truth about him, but I'm also certain that you don't love him as much as you think you do.'

'You're wrong! I do love him—I *do*!'

'No, you don't!' he contradicted harshly. 'You've been dazzled by his charming manner and glib tongue like so many others before you, but you don't love him.'

Samantha stared at him, her eyes dark with anger. 'I'm quite capable of looking after myself, but I fail to see what you're trying to achieve with all your insulting remarks.'

'I'm trying to make you see that what you feel for him is nothing more than infatuation,' he replied with galling confidence.

This was too much, and Samantha drew a shuddering breath, almost choking in her fury as she tilted her head upwards to face him defiantly. 'Brett Carrington, you bulldozed your way into my life without so much as a by-your-leave, but I will not have you dictating to me as to whom I should and should not love! How can you claim to know my feelings, and who gives you the right to make accusations against someone who isn't here to defend himself?'

'I presume you're referring to Clive Wilmot?'

His mockery did not escape her, and it only served to infuriate her more. 'You know very well I am!'

'I'm quite prepared to repeat my accusations with Clive Wilmot present, and it would give me the greatest pleasure to see him squirm.' There was a hard brutality in his features she had never seen before, but he recovered himself swiftly. 'Samantha, you're too good for him.'

'Don't make me laugh,' she said sarcastically.

'Will you marry me, Samantha?'

She stared at him in stunned silence for immeasurable seconds before she managed to gather her wits about her. 'You must be mad!' she blurted out. 'I wouldn't marry you if you were the last man on earth!'

Those firm lips twisted cynically. 'You won't marry Clive Wilmot either—all he'll do is to persuade you to become his mistress. He won't marry anyone unless he can benefit financially from the marriage.'

Samantha paled visibly. 'What a horrible thing to say!'

'Horrible things sometimes have to be said when

someone is too stubborn to take advice.'

'I refuse to listen to you!' she cried desperately, placing her hands against her ears to shut out his accusations and detestable insinuations. 'You've said quite enough!'

Cruel fingers latched on to her wrists and dragged her hands from her ears. 'If you won't listen to me, then I shall have to prove to you that your affections are misplaced.'

Not guessing his intentions, she was quite unprepared for the sudden onslaught on her emotions. Arms of steel held her with effortless ease against the muscular hardness of his body, while his lips found hers unguarded. This was what she had feared, and now she knew the reason why. His kiss ripped through her defences, drawing a wild response from her that was terrifying as well as intoxicating while strange new emotions raced through her, engulfing her in their intensity. She was vaguely conscious of the fact that she had to resist, but she had neither the will nor the strength to do anything other than cling to him and wish that this awe-inspiring moment would last for ever.

It seemed an eternity before Brett eventually raised his head, his eyes almost black with undisguised passion as he held hers captive. With hammering heart she saw him lower his head once more, and it was then that a spark of sanity flared within her.

'No! Please don't!' she begged hoarsely, but his arms merely tightened about her while his warm lips sought the hollow in her throat where a pulse throbbed frantically.

'Be truthful, Samantha, and admit that Clive's kisses have never aroused you the way mine have just done.'

She could not argue against such a blatant truth, for

not even during their most passionate embrace had Clive ever succeeded in stirring more than the surface of her emotions.

'Brett, stop it! You have no right——'

'I have as much right as Clive Wilmot,' he insisted, his hands warm and exciting against her back.

'No, no!' she whispered weakly.

'Yes, Samantha.' He raised his head then and she felt her defences slipping as she met the passionate ferocity of his gaze. 'Don't shut your mind to the truth.'

'I'm in love with Clive,' she insisted, but her voice sounded unconvincing to her own ears. 'Why won't you accept that fact and leave me alone?'

'You're trying very hard to convince yourself, aren't you?' Brett mocked her mercilessly.

'I don't have to convince myself. I know!'

'Do you, Samantha?' he asked with dangerous softness, lowering his dark head once more and creating havoc with her emotions as his lips claimed her in a devastating kiss that left no room for coherent thought. 'Are you very sure?'

How could she think clearly when his lips against her throat produced such tantalising sensations? She *had* to resist! She *had* to think of Clive!

Samantha struggled against him in an effort to avoid his lips. 'Don't, Brett. Oh, don't!'

'You're as innocent as a baby, my dear. You've never been more vitally alive than at this moment, and still you refuse to recognise it.' He released her with an abruptness that caused her to sway backwards against a chair, collapsing into it as her legs gave way. 'There's a difference, you know, between being in love ... and loving.'

Free of him now, Samantha found her pulse rate subsiding and she found her anger returning as she remarked with unaccustomed sarcasm, 'I had no idea that you were an authority on the subject!'

For one brief moment she feared that she might have gone too far, for flames of anger flickered momentarily in his dark eyes before he laughed harshly. 'All right, Samantha, you win. Please accept my apologies, although I can't say that I regret what I did. I enjoyed kissing you very much and I was absolutely serious when I asked you to marry me.'

Samantha gripped the edge of her seat as she stared up at him, her knuckles showing white through the skin as she made an effort to regain her composure. 'Why should someone like you want to marry a girl like me when there are plenty of eligible women from wealthy and influential families in the city from whom you could choose a wife who would suit you far more admirably than I would?'

'They would bore me to tears,' he announced mockingly as he bent down and imprisoned her in her chair. 'I would prefer to marry a small package of dynamite labelled Samantha Little.'

The ticking of the clock against the wall seemed to become louder, scraping along her already sensitive nerves, while his nearness disturbed her pulse rate and quickened her breath. 'I—I don't know what to say.'

'Say ... yes, Brett, I'll marry you.'

It would be so easy to say 'yes' to a man like Brett Carrington, she realised all at once. He was attractive, in a rugged sort of way, and he was wealthy, two factors which could turn any girl's head if she desired a marriage that would bring her wealth and prestige. If it was not for the fact that she was so unfalteringly sure of her love for Clive, it would have been very easy to say 'yes' to Brett, but she had to make herself believe that the emotions he had evoked within her had been purely physical, and nothing more.

'I can't, Brett. You know I can't.'

The firm mouth twisted slightly into a semblance of a smile. 'There's really nothing to stop you from marrying me.'

'Brett ... I'm sorry, but ... I don't love you,' she ended miserably, avoiding his eyes and the look of disbelief that glimmered through.

'We won't discuss the subject further at the moment,' she heard him say, much to her relief. 'Friends?'

'Yes, Brett,' she laughed self-consciously, 'as long as you don't expect more of me than friendship.'

'I don't give up that easily, Samantha,' he warned ominously. 'I usually get what I want, but for the time being I'm prepared to place the subject on ice.'

James Little arrived home late that evening to find Samantha waiting up for him in the darkened lounge.

'This makes a welcome change to find you waiting up for me,' he chuckled, switching on the reading lamp. He gestured towards the cigarette stub in the ashtray. 'I see you've had company. Brett Carrington?'

'Yes.' Samantha bit her lip nervously. 'Daddy, I have to talk to you.'

'Hm ... yes?'

'Brett asked me to marry him.'

'And?' her father asked with his back to her as he poured himself a whisky and splashed some soda into it.

'You don't seem surprised. Did you know he would propose?'

'No, but I suspected something like that.' He turned then, drink in his hand, and seated himself beside her on the couch. 'Did you accept?'

'No.'

'Because of the way you feel about Clive?'

'Yes.'

'Hm ...' James Little sipped thoughtfully at his drink before turning to face her. 'If it hadn't been for Clive—would you have accepted?'

'Daddy, that's not a fair question,' she rebuked him gently.

'Isn't it? Have I been mistaken in thinking you liked Brett?'

'I ... yes,' she admitted, surprising even herself. 'I can't help liking him, but I'm also afraid of him.'

Bushy eyebrows ascended above incredulous grey eyes. 'Afraid? Good heavens, why?'

'I've never met anyone like him before,' she explained tensely, recalling those moments in Brett's arms and how easily she had responded. 'Daddy, why should a man like Brett Carrington want to marry someone like myself? Why should he have bothered with me at all? It doesn't make sense. We met quite by chance, and all of a sudden my life is no longer my own. I had no particular wish to see him again, but I've been unable to shake him off,' she concluded, gesturing helplessly with her hands. 'Why, Daddy?'

James drank deeply on his whisky and stretched out his legs before venturing a reply. 'You don't suppose it might be because he's in love with you?'

'In love with me?' Samantha repeated, laughing cynically. 'Oh, no, Daddy. A man doesn't build up a reputation for being a confirmed bachelor only to be caught by someone as insignificant as myself.'

'You could be mistaken.'

'No, there has to be some other reason, I'm sure.'

'I was a confirmed bachelor until I met your mother.'

'But you're different, Daddy,' she insisted. 'You weren't arrogant, dictatorial and self-sufficient.'

'How do you know I wasn't all those things you just mentioned?' he chuckled suddenly, clearly amused by

her remarks. 'I was thirty-six when I marri
mother, and I was set in my ways as well as accusto
to doing just as I pleased. Age loses its significance
when you love someone.'

Samantha pressed her fingers against her closed eyelids in an effort to relieve the tired ache behind them.
'Oh, I don't know what to think. I'm confused and just
too tired to try to understand Brett Carrington's mo-
tives.'

'Samantha,' her father began tentatively, breaking
the troubled silence that lingered in the air, 'would
you consider a move to Cape Town?'

Samantha removed her fingers from her eyes and
blinked rapidly at her father to clear her vision. 'Cape
Town?'

'The firm has offered me a transfer to our new Cape
Town branch. It will be a challenge for me, but not an
absolute necessity, so ...'

His voice trailed off into silence as the world began
to rock beneath her. 'Would you like to go very much?'

James gestured self-consciously. 'My dear, at my age
I'm perhaps too old to accept challenge and changes.'

'Will I have to go with you?' she asked the dreaded
question.

'I would prefer it,' he replied instantly, lowering her
hopes to a level of desperation. 'It will, of course, mean
a separation from Clive.'

'Yes ...' Torn between her devotion for her father
and her love for Clive, she hesitated briefly before continuing: 'Daddy, you could go without me. I ...'

James shook his head firmly. 'You're only twenty and
I would be shirking my responsibilities if I left you
behind here in Port Elizabeth.'

'Daddy, there are plenty of girls my age who live
alone,' she argued hopefully.

while I'm still alive, and until
ill remain my responsibility,' he
ntly. 'Is it so important that you
Wilmot?'

y, but I'm ... in love with Clive.' She
was   herself for her slight hesitation when
she saw   er's curious glance.

'You're sure of this?'

'I've never doubted it.'

A peculiar smile appeared about her father's mouth
that sent her scurrying to her room after a hasty 'goodnight' peck on his cheek. Was she still so very sure of
her love for Clive, she finally asked herself as she slid
between the sheets and lay staring into the darkness, or
was she stubbornly clinging to something which no
longer existed? She had to admit, however reluctantly,
that during those moment's in Brett's arms she had not
been at all sure of her love for Clive! Her insistence
had merely assumed a form of defence at the time.
Now, away from Brett's disturbing influence, she told
herself that she was absolutely sure of her feelings. Loving was trusting, and she had to believe in Clive despite
all the ridiculous accusations made against him.

She turned her face into the pillow and her thoughts
turned inexplicably to Brett. She had to forget him;
forget that he ever aroused emotions she had not
dreamed that she possessed, but her hammering heart
mocked her childish determination.

Samantha and her father were having breakfast in the
kitchen when the telephone rang on that Saturday
morning Clive was due to arrive.

'I'll get it,' her father said hastily, excusing himself
from the table and leaving her to wonder why he had
appeared so agitated. Without intending to, she found

herself listening curiously to the disjointed and intriguing conversation.

'Yes ... no ... she won't agree to that ... yes, of course. I'm not very happy about shifting my job on to someone else ... yes, I know I can trust you implicitly, and that's why ... yes, thank you.'

The strangely guarded conversation ended abruptly and Samantha was instantly alert. What did it all mean? she wondered, frowning down at the omelette she had allowed to become cold in her plate.

'Sorry about that,' her father apologised distractedly as he resumed his seat. He was clearly agitated and deep in thought, but he made no effort to explain as he poured himself a fresh cup of coffee.

'Something wrong at the office?' she asked.

'What? Oh ... yes. Something to do with work,' he muttered, avoiding her eyes.

'Are you accepting the transfer to Cape Town?' she probed tentatively, not particularly wanting to renew the subject.

'I haven't decided yet, but I have until Monday to reach a final decision.'

'If you do accept, how soon do you have to leave?'

'Immediately.'

Samantha's eyes widened considerably, but she remained silent as she piled the breakfast dishes into the sink and started washing up.

'I'll help you,' James offered, but Samantha shook her head firmly.

'It's your day off, Daddy, so make yourself comfortable in the lounge with the morning paper while I get on with it.'

She had to think and decide what to do about this new development. To accompany her father would mean parting from Clive for long periods, and to insist

on remaining would merely jeopardise her father's op-
portunities, because he would refuse to go without her.
She was trapped; cornered by circumstances and unable to find the way out. Everything was against her
and Clive, but it merely made her more determined
that they would succeed in proving everyone wrong.
Clive was kind and gentle as well as passionate, and
she would not exchange him for someone with a fiery
temperament like Brett Carrington who could sweep
her emotions into a turmoil with the merest glance.

Samantha was eventually vacuum-cleaning the
lounge carpet when the doorbell chimed shortly after
ten that morning. She switched off the cleaner and
finally flung open the door with a sigh of irritation.

'Good morning, Samantha.'

It was only the man who had the power to unnerve
her completely—Brett Carrington!

CHAPTER FOUR

THE heavy thudding of her heart almost choked her as she stared up at Brett. Immaculate as always in a beige lightweight suit and matching tie, he looked tanned and virile, and arrogantly self-assured as he stepped past her.

'What do you want?' Samantha demanded rudely, closing the door to keep out the draught coming up from the stairs.

He ignored her lack of courtesy with a touch of mockery in his glance. 'It's a lovely morning and I've come to take you for a drive out into the country.'

Just like that! Samantha thought angrily. She had not seen him since the evening he had asked her to marry him, and now he just arrived and calmly stated that he would be taking her for a drive. The arrogance of the man!

'I'm afraid it's out of the question,' Samantha told him, avoiding his glance as she returned the vacuum cleaner to its place in the passage cupboard. 'I'm meeting Clive at the airport and his plane arrives at noon.'

'In that case I'll drive you there.'

She stared at him open-mouthed, but she was prevented from telling him exactly what she thought of him as her father emerged from the lounge.

'Good morning, Brett. I couldn't help overhearing that last remark, and I think it would be an excellent idea if you drove Samantha to the airport. My car's been giving me quite a bit of trouble these past few days.'

How dared they stand there and calmly organise her life as if she was of no significance? she fumed, mentally stamping her foot as her glance went from one to the other. Besides, there had been nothing wrong with her father's car when she had used it the previous evening to call on Gillian at her home.

'I would prefer——' she began.

'Go and powder your nose, then we can drive out there now,' Brett interrupted smoothly. 'I have something to show you that might interest you.'

Samantha glanced helplessly at her father, but he gestured firmly that she should do as she was told, and with an infuriated shrug she swept past them. She could hear their subdued voices in the lounge, but at that moment she was too angry to be particularly interested in their conversation. Perhaps, if she had been a little more observant, the pattern of her immediate future might have been drastically altered by the knowledge she would have gained if she had listened in on their conversation.

'Take good care of her,' James instructed as they were about to leave, and Samantha stared at her father in surprise as she felt the pressure of his arm about her shoulders and his lips against her cheek. What on earth was the matter with him? Could he be ill?

'You have my word on that,' Brett promised gravely, and this was even more disturbing.

'Brett's only driving me to the airport to meet Clive, you know,' Samantha remarked with forced amusement, endeavouring to ease the tension which hovered vibrantly in the air. 'I'm not going to the ends of the earth.'

James smiled at her with unaccustomed tenderness. 'It's my privilege to be concerned about my daughter.'

Samantha could not prevent the smile that curved

her lovely mouth as she reached up and planted a kiss on his rough cheek. 'I'm a big girl now, Daddy. *Tot siens.*'

'Goodbye, Samantha.'

Brett hustled her from the flat and, to her surprise, it was not his silver Jaguar that stood at the entrance, but a sleek black Mercedes. A white-coated, peak-capped chauffeur jumped to attention as they approached and opened the rear door with a flourish. Sitting in the cushioned luxury of the back seat beside Brett, she sent him a questioning glance.

'I occasionally employ the services of my chauffeur,' he explained offhandedly. 'It makes a welcome change to relax and enjoy the scenery.'

'That sounds funny coming from someone who always has to be in command of every situation,' Samantha remarked, unable to keep the sarcasm from her voice as the car pulled away from the curb, heading towards the centre of the city. They were obviously taking the longest route to the airport, round the Mayor's Garden, down towards South End and past King's Beach.

'You will discover, Samantha, that I'm human with human feelings like everyone else,' he informed her mildly as they left the city traffic behind. 'No one is perfect.'

He spoke as if had every intention of continuing their relationship, but she would have to disillusion him, and at once, she decided, scraping together her courage.

'Brett, there's something I want to make quite clear to you,' she began, turning in her seat to face him. 'I don't want to see you again after today.'

She had expected mockery or heavy sarcasm, but she

found herself unable to argue with his calm but authoritative reply.

'Do you mind if we discontinue this discussion until
we're alone?'

Samantha fell silent, not paying much attention to
their surroundings as she became aware instead of his
hand lying on the seat between them so close to her
own. It was a hand with well-kept fingernails and fine
black hair on the back. It indicated strength and the
capability to crush, or to spark off emotions she preferred not to dwell on.

A car shot across the red light at the robot on the
beach front and Brett's driver swerved violently, nar-
rowly avoiding a collision with a stationary car while
at the same time trying to avoid the car that continued
on its way without stopping. The suddenness of it all
flung Samantha against Brett and his arms closed about
her instantly.

'Are you all right?'

'Yes—yes, I think so,' she stammered, but the pressure of his arms did not diminish as she trembled with
shock.

'That damn fool, whoever he is, could have caused
a nasty accident,' he exclaimed angrily, glancing at his
chauffeur. 'Joseph, did you get the number of that
car?'

'No, sir. I'm sorry, sir.'

'He ought to be taken off the road permanently,'
Brett continued harshly, but left the subject there.

Samantha extricated herself carefully from his arms
and straightened, but the whole unfortunate episode
had unnerved her so severely that violent tremors
shook through her body. She had seen that car seconds
before it had disappeared down Humewood Road and
it had been Clive's—or one very like his. But Clive was

still in Cape Town, wasn't he? Could he have returned on an earlier flight without telling her? But why? She drew a shuddering breath and admonished herself severely for the doubts she was entertaining. It was all Brett's fault, she decided angrily. If he had not persisted with his nasty insinuations she would never have considered the possibility that that car had been driven by Clive. Clive was still in Cape Town, she told herself firmly, and he would be arriving with the twelve o'clock flight as he had said he would.

When they finally reached the airport, Brett helped her alight from the car and kept his hand on her arm as they entered the building. 'There's still plenty of time. We can order a strong pot of tea in the restaurant.'

Without waiting for a reply, he ushered her in that direction. He found a table close to the window and placed their order as the waitress appeared, then an uneasy silence lingered between them until their tea was eventually served.

Samantha poured and they drank in silence for a moment, the strongly brewed tea steadying her nerves and bringing the colour back to her cheeks.

'Are you looking forward to seeing Clive again?' Brett asked abruptly, taking a cigarette from his cigarette case and lighting it carefully.

'Very much.'

'A pity.'

Samantha placed her cup in the saucer with a clatter. 'If you're going to start being unpleasant——'

'Did you know your eyes become a deep violet blue when you're angry or emotionally disturbed?' He leaned closer to observe her and there was devilment in his eyes. 'It's most extraordinary.'

Taken aback, Samantha hovered between anger and

embarrassment. 'You're the most disconcerting man I've ever met!'

'Do you find the truth disconcerting?'

'When it's aimed at me personally, yes.'

'Doesn't Clive ever tell you how beautiful you are? That you have hair like spun gold, truly remarkable eyes, a small perfectly chiselled nose, and the most delightful lips that were made to be kissed?'

Her cheeks were flaming by the time he had concluded his summary and she hastily lowered her glance to avoid the mockery in his eyes.

'Must you say these things?' she managed finally.

'I find your blushes intriguing and your innocence captivating,' Brett persisted, his glance no longer mocking but completely unfathomable. 'Surely you're not so completely unaware of your alluring appearance?'

Samantha bit her lip nervously, not sure just how to take him in this frame of mind. 'I don't want to appear alluring.'

Brett laughed derisively. 'Don't say that as though it were some terrible sin! If Adam hadn't found Eve alluring, where would this human race be today?'

A smile tugged at the corners of her mouth but it disappeared swiftly when she noticed the sudden sternness of his expression. His moods altered swiftly, she had noticed. One minute he would shower her with attention, however mocking, and the next he would appear almost bored with the trend of the conversation. It was most confusing, she decided, pushing her empty cup aside and glancing through the window at the Boeing taxiing on to the runway.

'Have you ever flown before?' he asked suddenly, and she felt a nervous flutter at the base of her throat.

'No.'

'Would you like to?'

Samantha fingered the tablecloth absently. 'When the opportunity presents itself, yes.'

'I have a small aircraft out there. I could give you a taste of flying and have you back here in time to meet Wilmot.' His glance was persuasive. 'Shall we go?'

'I don't know. I——'

'You're not frightened, are you?' Brett mocked her, crushing his cigarette into the ashtray.

'No!' she lied bravely, but she was determined that he should not be aware of the quaking feeling which had gripped her insides.

'Let's go, then.'

Samantha barely had time to snatch up her handbag as he settled the account and ushered her through the building and out on to the tarmac. The small aircraft turned out to be a sleek four-seater, painted white and trimmed with red. Brett climbed aboard ahead of her and then turned.

'Give me your hand,' he instructed and, as she did so, she was thankful that she had chosen to wear her slacks instead of the narrow skirt she had originally selected.

Her hands fumbled with the seat belt and Brett was forced to lean across from behind the controls to secure the fastener for her.

'Ready?' he questioned impatiently.

'Y-yes,' she managed, swallowing convulsively as her throat tightened.

'Right, here we go.'

He placed the earphones on his head as the engine sprang to life and Samantha could feel the tremendous vibration beneath her while he requested permission to take off. This was followed by an aeronautical discussion she was unable to understand and then, suddenly, they were moving forward, taxiing out on to the appropriate runway. It seemed an endless, timeless journey before Brett pulled out the throttle and the engine began to speed up. They moved forward now, gathering speed, and Samantha gripped her seat as the earth suddenly fell away beneath them.

She closed her eyes tightly as they gained height, wishing at that moment that she had been less brave when he had suggested this excursion.

'You can open your eyes now,' he shouted above the roar of the engine, and she did so only to meet his mocking glance. He was fully aware of her nervousness and certainly enjoying her discomfort. 'Relax, Samantha, and enjoy it. I don't intend to frighten you with aerobatic stunts.'

'I wouldn't put that past you,' she countered, gritting her teeth.

'Don't tempt me, my dear.'

It had been a warning and Samantha knew better than to pursue the subject. She glanced tentatively through the window to see the teeming city beneath them, the Campanile, standing almost at the entrance to the busy harbour as a memorial to the 1820 British settlers, and the tall buildings along Main Street which now looked peculiarly small from that height. Then, as they left everything of structural interest behind them, she gradually began to relax and enjoy the surrounding countryside below. Her fear overcome, it was a fantastic experience being able to survey everything from that height. It was a clear, warm day and the visibility stretched for seemingly endless kilometres, affording her the breathtaking view of the valleys and rivers winding their way among the hills, flowing past picturesque little villages nestling on their banks. This was the Sundays River Valley—citrus country.

'If you look directly ahead of us you'll see the Addo

Elephant Park,' Brett interrupted her thoughts, pointing at the dense bush below.

'Have we come this far in so short a time?'

'Yes. Does it surprise you?'

'It does, but ...' Samantha bit her lip and glanced nervously at her wristwatch, 'shouldn't we be returning?'

'Why the hurry, Samantha?' he mocked, meeting her anxious eyes. 'I thought you were enjoying yourself?'

'I am, but will you have enough fuel to get us back to Port Elizabeth?'

Brett raised a satirical eyebrow. 'Are you doubting my capabilities as a pilot?'

'No,' she replied with nervous haste. 'No, of course not.'

'You're perfectly safe with me,' he announced drily, returning his attention to the numerous dials in front of him.

Samantha remained silent for a considerable length of time, but she could no longer restrain herself when they flew over the Suurberg Mountains with Lake Mentz clearly in the distance.

'Brett, it's almost eleven-thirty,' she protested weakly. 'We must turn back now or I shan't be in time to meet Clive.'

'I'm afraid Clive will have to do without his welcoming committee,' he informed her smoothly. 'There's something I want to show you.'

Samantha felt a chill of fear that made her skin crawl as she stared at him aghast. 'Brett, you can't do this! Please turn back!'

'I'm sorry, Samantha,' he replied without a trace of regret as he glanced at the dials. 'I have just enough fuel to get us safely to our destination.'

'And where, may I ask, is that?' she demanded with heavy sarcasm.

Brett glanced at her briefly, but his expression conveyed nothing. 'You'll see for yourself in less than fifteen minutes.'

Samantha clenched her hands in her lap, fighting against the uncontrollable anger that raged through her. 'I suppose you think you've been very clever!'

'Yes, I think so.'

Realisation dawned with a swiftness that took her breath away. 'You deliberately planned this trip so I wouldn't be at the airport to meet Clive. Didn't you?'

His smile was infuriating. 'That was a very clever piece of deduction, if I may say so.'

She sagged helplessly against the firm backrest. 'I don't know what you hope to gain by this, but I can tell you now that, whatever it is, you won't succeed.'

'We shall see, Samantha,' he replied abruptly, his lips tightening and the square chin jutting out stubbornly. 'Sit tight, I'm going in to land.'

Samantha closed her eyes hastily as the tarmac rose to meet them. There was a bump as the wheels touched down and the revving of the engine gradually ceased its deafening roar, and she opened her eyes with a feeling of relief to discover that they were taxiing towards a hanger beside which a Land-Rover was parked. The occupant of the open Land-Rover waved excitedly and Brett returned the gesture, a smile of pleasure lighting up his stern features that made him look curiously younger.

'That's Lucas,' he told her, cutting the engine and undoing his seat belt. 'He looks after the vehicles as well as being a general all-rounder.'

He helped her down off the aircraft before turning to the coloured man who was approaching them with a welcoming smile on his weather beaten face. He was dressed simply in khaki drill trousers and shirt, with an old slouch hat pulled down over his eyes to guard them against the glaring sunlight. Brett shook hands with him and then drew Samantha to his side. 'Lucas, this is Miss Samantha Little.'

'Glad to know you, Miss Samantha,' Lucas said, touching his hat respectfully before turning again to Brett. 'The Madam said I was to bring the Master straight to the house. No nonsense.'

Brett nodded soberly. 'I bet dear old Aunt Emma has worked herself up into a stew about the message I sent her this morning.'

'Stew is the right word, Master Brett,' Lucas chuckled as they climbed into the Land-Rover.

All this, Samantha supposed, had something to do with her unexpected arrival. It was obvious that Aunt Emma, whoever she might be, was not at all thrilled at the prospect of having an unwanted guest thrust upon her, for however brief a period. She glanced at her watch, sighing inwardly. It was past midday and Clive would already have arrived in Port Elizabeth, she realised, but she would just have to bear this slight delay caused by Brett and look forward instead to seeing Clive that evening.

Having made this decision, she glanced about her with interest for the first time. This was the Karoo, she realised, taking in the scrub-covered country, but she had no idea exactly where they were. The Land-Rover bumped unexpectedly over an uneven piece of ground and Samantha grabbed at the back of Brett's seat to steady herself.

'Sorry about this,' he said tersely, turning in his seat. 'The recent rains have played havoc with the road. We're almost there.'

Up ahead among the trees she caught sight of a house, but her view was partially hampered by Brett's dark head and broad shoulders directly in front of her. They passed through a white-painted stone arch with the name, *Carrington's Post*, engraved impressively on it in large black letters. So this was one of his farms, she thought as they drove through an avenue of poplar trees, but why on earth should he have brought her here?

They emerged from the welcoming shadow of the trees and Samantha drew her breath in sharply as the homestead loomed up ahead. It was large and impressive with a wide stoep on the north side of the house, where gravel paths wound their way through an ornamental garden that gave her the curious impression of an oasis in the semi-desert. All this she noticed in one sweeping, startled glance as the Land-Rover crunched to a halt at the foot of the stone steps leading up to what was obviously the front door. This in itself was a work of art and craftsmanship. Circular steps led up to the heavy oak door above which a circular roof, trimmed with wrought-iron, rested on carved stone pillars. Carved into the stone just above the door were two lions facing each other, their tails lashing the air, their fangs bared and their claws unsheathed to do battle.

Was this symbolic of the Carrington family? Samantha wondered, experiencing a sudden attack of nerves as she stood there beside Brett, trembling inwardly as his strong fingers closed about her arm. Lucas, knowing that he was no longer required, drove off in the Land-Rover as they mounted the steps.

'Welcome to my home, Samantha.'

'Your ... home?' she managed breathlessly, glancing up at him in surprise. The wind had whipped through his hair in the open Land-Rover and it fell heavily across his forehead. It made him look different somehow; less austere, but she was not deceived.

'This is my home when I'm not in the city,' he informed her in clipped tones. 'It has housed four generations of Carringtons, including myself, and it will also be the home of my children one day.'

His children! She had never thought to hear him speak of his children. Marriage and children were something one found difficult to associate with Brett Carrington, the confirmed bachelor.

The heavy oak door opened without a sound and a woman stood there, tall and erect in a black frock that hung well below her knees. Her grey hair was combed back from her face and rolled into a neat bun in the nape of her neck, while the only thing that was alive in her gaunt, marble-like features was the burning disapproval in her eyes.

'Aunt Emma!' Brett exclaimed, striding forward to plant a kiss on her thin cheek. He turned then and beckoned to Samantha. 'Let me introduce you. This is Samantha Little. Samantha ... my Aunt Emma Bryce, the only woman who has the audacity to imagine that I'll jump when she cracks the whip.'

His teasing remark did not lessen her disapproval as she acknowledged Samantha's timid greeting in a clear, remarkably pleasant voice. 'If you come this way I'll show you to your room, Miss Little. I'm sure you would like to freshen up before lunch.'

'Thank you,' Samantha murmured, glancing swiftly at Brett as she brushed passed him, but his expression remained inscrutable.

The silence was strained as she followed Emma Bryce into the magnificent hallway with its rosewood furniture and chandeliers hanging from the high ceiling, their steps making no sound on the carpeted staircase with its carved wooden balustrade. It was cool inside and Samantha shivered slightly as she wondered whether this woman was always so severe-looking, or whether it was as a result of the inconvenience caused by an unexpected guest, for Emma Bryce had certainly not gone out of her way to make her feel at all welcome.

She opened a door to one of the rooms on the upper floor and stood aside for Samantha to enter. The room was fully carpeted with an old-fashioned brass bed dominating the room. Samantha fingered the lace bedspread and then turned self-consciously towards the older woman.

'It's very beautiful,' she remarked, gesturing towards the bedspread. 'Did you make it, Mrs Bryce?'

'No. Brett's mother made it shortly before her death,' she replied abruptly, and then gestured towards a door leading off the room. 'The bathroom is through there. I'm sure you'll find everything you may need.'

'It's very kind of you to allow me the use of this room for the hour or so that I shall be here,' Samantha said politely.

Emma Bryce stared at her curiously, almost as if she were about to say something of importance, then she apparently changed her mind and reassumed her grim expression.

'When you're ready, come down to the dining-room, child. It's the first door to your right at the bottom of the stairs.'

Without giving Samantha the opportunity to thank her, she turned and closed the door behind her.

Samantha endeavoured to shrug off the uneasiness which had settled upon her and went through to the bathroom. This suite had obviously belonged to a woman, she guessed, glancing about her. Brett's sister? she wondered curiously as she washed her face and hands and made use of the hand towel placed at her disposal. Judging by the array of powders, bath oils and perfumes, the occupant of this room had had a truly feminine weakness for such luxuries.

She found her comb in her handbag and pulled it through her hair before touching up her make-up. On the dressing-table in the bedroom she discovered a brush and comb set with the initials N.C. engraved on them. So she had been right, she thought, in thinking that this had been his sister's room. What had she been like? she wondered curiously. And what had the initial N stood for? Nancy; Natalie? Norma, perhaps?

Samantha closed her handbag with a decisive snap. She had better not keep Brett and his aunt waiting or she might bring more than disapproval down upon her own head, she decided as she closed the bedroom door softly behind her and found her way down to the hall. As she hovered at the entrance to the dining-room, the sound of raised voices from the opposite direction drew her attention. Brett and his aunt were obviously disagreeing on some major issue, because the argument was heated. Samantha quelled the sudden desire to eavesdrop and entered the dining-room instead to admire the priceless silverware and the solid teak furniture.

The minutes ticked by on the clock above the dresser and she turned idly towards the window. What could they be arguing about? she wondered curiously before losing herself in the beauty of the garden. So engrossed was she in this sunlit paradise that she jumped violently when Brett spoke beside her.

'My apologies for keeping you waiting, Samantha,' he said brusquely, sending a glance in his aunt's direction that conveyed a clear warning. 'There was an urgent matter we had to discuss.'

'That's quite all right,' Samantha assured him uncomfortably. 'I've been admiring your lovely view of the garden.'

'All the rooms, except those on the south side, have a view of the garden,' Emma Bryce told her, making her statement sound like a rebuke. 'Shall we have lunch?'

The air of hostility which prevailed made lunch an uncomfortable necessity. Samantha ate very little under the close scrutiny of Emma Bryce. What thoughts lay behind those curious grey eyes? she wondered. Was the fact that Brett had brought a female guest to Carrington's Post so unusual, or had their violent argument before lunch not concerned her at all? Whatever the reason, Samantha decided eventually, it had put neither of them in a sociable mood. Brett maintained an angry silence throughout the meal, and his aunt's complexion was a shade paler than on their arrival.

Tea was served in the living-room with its massive stone fireplace and deep, comfortable armchairs with their padded arm-rests and crocheted lace coverings. Expensive porcelain vases adorned the carved tables against the walls as well as a colourful vase of flowers on the low table in the centre of the room. It was a homely room, but the austere atmosphere caused by its occupants brought a chill to it which it did not deserve.

'Do you like my home, Samantha?' Brett asked unexpectedly, arresting her glance.

'The little I've seen of it I find very beautiful,' she admitted readily, her back muscles tense from perching nervously on the edge of her chair, almost as if she were ready for flight.

'Let me show you the ornamental garden,' he suggested, drawing her to her feet. 'It's Aunt Emma's pride and joy.'

It was obvious that he was making an effort to break the ice between them, but Emma Bryce maintained a stony silence and Brett merely shrugged carelessly as he steered Samantha through the double glass doors on to the stoep.

'It's like an oasis in the desert,' she echoed her original thoughts as she stood beside Brett, allowing her gaze to wander in among the carefully tended shrubs and flowering succulents.

He took her arm as they walked through the garden and she found herself strolling beneath shady trees, crossing sturdy ornamental bridges beneath which a carefully contrived stream flowed, and finally hovering ecstatically beside a lily pond in which the goldfish swam lazily beneath the circular flat leaves in search of food.

'It's beautiful!' she exclaimed with sincerity, glancing up to find Brett observing her with tolerant amusement, an unlit cigarette between his fingers. Embarrassed, she rose from her kneeling position and lowered her glance. 'You must find my enthusiasm boring. I'm sorry.'

'Sincere enthusiasm is never boring, Samantha, it's enchanting.' He gestured towards the bench beneath the oak tree. 'Let's sit down.'

Seated beside him on the wooden bench, Samantha recalled the incidents leading up to this enforced visit to his home, and the beauty of the garden was temporarily forgotten.

'All right, Brett, you've had your fun,' she reminded him calmly. 'Will you take me back to Port Elizabeth now that I've seen your home?'

Brett took his time lighting his cigarette before turning to face her, and there was a firmness about his jaw that unnerved her. 'I'm afraid, Samantha, I neglected to tell you that you'll be staying here for a while.'

For several labouring seconds Samantha was conscious only of the heavy beat of her heart as she stared at him incredulously, every vestige of colour draining from her face and leaving her chilled to the marrow.

'You're joking, naturally,' she heard herself say in a choked voice.

'I've never been more serious.'

'But I can't stay here!'

'Why not?'

'My father——'

'You're here with your father's knowledge and complete approval.'

The world tilted crazily about her as she struggled to grasp his unbelievable statement. She clutched at the bench beneath her for support and blinked rapidly in an effort to bring his face into focus. 'You mean you planned this . . . abduction . . . between the two of you?'

'Exactly. I telephoned him this morning to tell him that everything had been arranged.'

'B-but w-why?'

Brett drew hard on his cigarette and then crushed the remainder beneath the heel of his expensive shoe. 'Your father and I both felt it would be in your own interest if you didn't see Clive Wilmot again . . . at least, not until you've ridded yourself of the ridiculous notion that you're in love with him.'

Anger came to her rescue and sent her blood racing vibrantly through her veins. 'I don't suppose it occurred to either of you that I might not want to rid myself of the idea that I love Clive?'

His eyebrows rose mockingly. 'I'm afraid, Samantha, that until you do you'll remain here at Carrington's Post.'

Samantha felt like slapping that smug, self-satisfied

look off his face, but her fear of the consequences kept her trembling hands tightly locked in her lap. 'You and my father must have been crazy to think that you could keep me here against my will!' she said furiously, grasping hopefully at the final straw available to her. 'There's my job, for instance. I can't just stay away like this.'

Brett's lips twisted cynically. 'You no longer have a job, because I took the liberty of having you replaced. I had to take your friend Gillian into my confidence, and she assisted me to find someone appropriate.'

It was like a stunning blow between the eyes, but it also explained Gillian's peculiar behaviour during the past week. Samantha sagged weakly against the back of the bench and lowered her lashes swiftly to veil the tears of helplessness which stung her eyes.

'You've thought of everything, haven't you?' she said dully, the shrill sound of the cicadas in the afternoon heat scraping along her sensitive nerves.

'I don't believe in half measures,' he replied mercilessly. 'Your clothes and personal possessions are being packed for you at this moment, but they won't arrive before tomorrow. Until then you'll have to make do with what remains of my sister's wardrobe.' His glance swept over her momentarily. 'She was considerably taller than you, although just as slight, but I dare say you won't mind the unavoidable inconvenience until your own things arrive.'

CHAPTER FIVE

A PROFOUND silence followed Brett's remark—a silence during which Samantha assimilated the shocking realisation that he was in deadly earnest about keeping her there for an unspecified period. Her trembling hands fluttered nervously in a pleading gesture, only to fall back limply into her lap. She seldom smoked except in moments of dire stress and this, she decided, was one of them.

'May I have a cigarette, please?'

Brett's expression was unfathomable as he calmly opened his cigarette case and extended it towards her. She selected one and rolled the cigarette nervously between her fingers until he held the lighter towards her, his hand cupped about the flame. She coughed slightly at the first draw, but soon experienced its soothing effect on her shattered nerves.

'Was asking me to marry you part of this diabolical plan?' she asked finally when she was in complete control of her voice.

'Not exactly,' he smiled briefly, 'but it would have been simpler if you had accepted. There would have been no need then to abduct you.'

'It amazes me to think that you would have gone to the extent of giving up your freedom to wreck my relationship with Clive,' she remarked with a touch of sarcasm.

'No, my dear, you're wrong,' he said with quiet determination. 'I asked you to marry me because I wanted you for my wife. I still aim to persuade you to accept my proposal.'

'Why?'

Brett shrugged carelessly. 'Let's say you're the only woman I've ever met who I feel sure would suit me admirably as a wife.'

Samantha felt curiously hurt. 'You make it all sound so cold-blooded!'

'Perhaps it is,' he admitted icily, removing the unsmoked cigarette from her passive fingers with a distasteful expression on his face and promptly disposing of it. 'There's something else I have to tell you. Your father has accepted that transfer to Cape Town, and he leaves on Monday.'

'How very convenient,' she remarked, trembling with renewed anger. 'I feel like a cumbersome, erring child, shuttled from one parent to the other when the burden has become too uncomfortable to bear.'

'You're not a child, Samantha, you're a woman.' His voice sent a chill up her spine. 'Likewise, I'm not your parent, but the man who hopes to marry you some day when you've acknowledged your infatuation and realised that you're as yet unawakened.'

'I'll never marry you, and I'll get away from here somehow!'

Brett leaned closer to her, his manner threatening. 'I must warn you, my dear, that you will not be allowed to escape. My staff have been instructed to keep an eye on you and, as there is no necessity for me to return to the city within the next month, I intend keeping an eye on you personally as an added precaution.'

'A month! A whole month!' she cried in disbelief. 'You can't keep me here that long?'

For seemingly endless seconds his dark eyes pinned her ruthlessly to her seat and not for the first time did she notice the peculiar colouring of his eyes. The dark brown eyes with the flecks of gold gave one that impression of leaping flames as the sunlight caught them. Beautiful eyes, she thought irrationally even as he spoke harshly. 'I'll keep you here much longer if you persist with your ridiculous notions.'

'I hate you, Brett Carrington,' she said with feeling, 'and I think both you and my father have behaved despicably!'

'We've acted in your interest alone.'

'My interest and my happiness lies with Clive, and nothing will alter that,' she argued hotly.

'A bold statement, Samantha, but a foolish one,' he claimed mockingly, drawing her to her feet. 'Come, you're overwrought and distressed. I suggest you lie down for a while until I send someone to call you down for tea.'

'I don't want to lie down, thank you.'

'Don't be childish, Samantha.' His rebuke was like a whiplash. 'Allow me to know what's best for you.'

'If you think I'm going to sit back meekly and allow you to carry out this disgusting plan of yours, then you're mistaken,' she informed him, lifting her chin defiantly. 'I shall fight you all the way.'

'I've always admired spirit, Samantha,' he laughed softly, 'and I would have been extremely disappointed if you'd merely accepted everything without a murmur.'

'You're insufferable!' she fumed and, turning, fled light-footed along the path, her eyes blinded once more by helpless tears of rage.

There was not a soul in sight when she entered the homestead. The tea cups had been removed from the living-room and a silence had descended upon the house as though everything had ceased to function after the midday heat. It was obviously the general practice for everyone to have a rest when the lunch was over, but it was a habit Samantha had never been able to cultivate.

She found her room without much difficulty and discovered that someone had drawn the curtains against the afternoon sun, leaving it pleasurably cool. The old-fashioned bed with its feather mattress looked inviting and Samantha finally succumbed to the invitation, slipping off her shoes and lying fully clothed on the bed after removing the exquisite lace bedspread.

'Oh, Clive!' she thought in anguish, 'How are we going to endure this unnecessary parting? How am I ever going to convince Brett that what we feel for each other is sincere?'

She turned her face to bury it in the pillow and, to her surprise, saw something she had not noticed before. Beside her bed, on a small table, stood a telephone. Clive would be at his flat and she could telephone him there. He would come and fetch her at once, and there would be nothing the mighty Mr Brett Carrington could do about it. She lifted the receiver, her heart racing with excitement, but the next instant the dialling tone was interrupted by a sharp click, to be followed by an ominous silence.

'Samantha,' Brett's voice came clearly over the line and she felt her nerves vibrating, 'your telephone is connected with mine here in the study, and also with the one in the hall. If you're thinking of telephoning Wilmot and asking for his assistance—forget it. I left a note at his flat informing him that you're here and he should have received it by now. He won't do a thing to help you.'

Samantha found her voice with difficulty. 'What makes you think that Clive won't come to my aid if I should ask him?'

'I know Clive Wilmot, but if you would like proof, then go ahead and phone him,' Brett remarked in a bored-sounding voice, replacing the receiver and leaving her for several seconds with nothing but the sound of the dialling tone in her ear.

Clive *would* come. Of course he would come! She argued mentally with herself, but the annoying fear that Brett's supposition might be confirmed made her replace the receiver as though it had suddenly burnt her fingers.

She supposed Brett must have heard her replacing the receiver without dialling and she could imagine that infuriating look of self-satisfaction on his usually immobile face. He had won this round. He had succeeded very cleverly in sowing a seed of doubt in her mind, and she hated him with an intensity that shook her slender frame.

She fell back against the pillows and closed her eyes, her hands clenched tightly against her sides. Without intending to, she saw again Brett's peculiar eyes and the way he had looked at her in the garden. He had succeeded in penetrating her defences, his eyes searching deeply and disturbingly into her soul, leaving her curiously defenceless and vaguely aware of something she could not put a name to.

Samantha literally shook herself free of these thoughts and wondered instead exactly how she had been such a fool to allow herself to be trapped into this slightly mediaeval situation. It was unheard-of in this modern century that a girl could be carried off in this way by a knight on a white charger to his castle in some secluded spot in the country. She giggled with rising hysteria as she thought of Brett as the knight in question, his small aircraft representing the white charger, and his home, Carrington's Post, as the castle. It was ludicrous! But the romance of the situation did not escape her, and her hammering heart told her that she was a fraud.

Brett Carrington had a forceful, magnetic personality; he was not the kind of man to be overlooked or underestimated, she realised again. He made his presence felt by those around him and he was decisive in his actions. However distasteful she found these thoughts she was forced to admit that Clive could not compare with Brett in this respect. Clive was handsome, suave and charming. He was passionate and petulant, but he was fun. He was, at times, like a tiresome child, but he was—romance. Brett, to the contrary, was mature in his approach to life, and there had been nothing peevish about him when she had struggled free of his embrace that evening he had proposed marriage so unexpectedly. Neither had there been anything immature about the way he had held and kissed her. He had been masterful and overpowering in his method, and it had taken all her will-power not to give way completely.

Her cheeks flamed suddenly as she remembered those moments. Brett had said that he had every intention of persuading her to accept his proposal of marriage. Would he use the same method of persuasion? she wondered irrationally, burying her face in the pillow as her skin tingled with the mere thought of those firm lips against her own.

No, it would be so easy to forget Clive; to give up the struggle against emotions that were becoming too powerful for her to control. She had to fight! she decided firmly. Brett had warned her against Clive, but she was in more imminent danger with Brett. With Clive she had been strong in mind and heart, but with Brett she was continually overcome by an inexplicable weakness, and awe-inspiring awareness that he could

bend her to his will as easily as bending a sapling between his fingers.

Brett was not in the living-room that afternoon when
Samantha went down for tea. She found Emma Bryce
alone, seated in an upright chair with the tea trolley
beside her.

'Have I kept you waiting?' Samantha asked apologetically as the woman glanced up, but Emma Bryce
shook her grey head and began to pour. Samantha
glanced about her expectantly. 'Isn't Brett coming
down for tea?'

'Brett has asked me to make his apologies,' the
woman said, handing Samantha her tea and gesturing
that she should help herself to milk and sugar. 'He's
taken one of the horses to make an inspection tour of
the new grazing camps. He's always preferred going on
horseback to taking one of the Land-Rovers.'

Samantha felt curiously deflated while at the same
time she was thankful for the opportunity to speak to
Brett's aunt alone.

'Mrs Bryce, I suppose you know Brett's reason for
bringing me here?' she began tentatively.

'Yes, I know.'

'Am I right in assuming that you don't approve of
the whole idea?' Samantha searched her face and was
surprised to see those gaunt features softening considerably. 'Is that the reason for the argument between Brett
and yourself before lunch?'

'You're very astute, my dear,' Emma Bryce said at
length, squaring her shoulders and avoiding Samantha's glance. 'I disagreed most strongly with my nephew
on the subject. He has no right to interfere in the lives
of others simply because Nadine . . .'

'Nadine?' Samantha questioned sharply as her voice
trailed off guiltily. 'Who's Nadine?'

'Brett's sister,' the older woman told her abruptly. 'She died three years ago.'

'What has Nadine to do with my being here?' Samantha persisted curiously, certain now that there was more to this whole situation than what Brett had led her to believe.

'Nothing,' Emma Bryce said, and Samantha was surprised to discover that the woman was decidedly uncomfortable about the way the conversation was developing. 'You know Brett's reasons for wanting to keep you here.'

Samantha decided against pursuing the subject and instead she asked: 'Mrs Bryce, will you help me to get away from here? Please?'

There was absolute silence for several seconds before Brett's aunt placed her empty cup in the tray with an unnecessary clatter.

'My dear girl, as much as I dislike the idea of Brett meddling in your life, I can't go against his wishes. Brett, like his father before him, is master of this household and everything that goes with it.' For the second time Samantha noticed a softening in the grey eyes and a gentleness about the mouth that had been nothing but firmly compressed since their arrival before lunch. 'Even I must obey him,' she added, and there was unexpected humour in the glance that held Samantha's. 'After all, you're here with your father's approval.'

So Emma Bryce was not such an iceberg as she had originally suspected, Samantha thought with a feeling of immense relief. 'What am I going to do?' she sighed.

'There's nothing you can do but accept the situation as gracefully as possible. Antagonising Brett will merely make matters worse for you.' She smiled now, transforming her features completely. 'More tea, Samantha?'

'No thank you.' Samantha returned the smile with a

heavy heart and rose to her feet. 'May I walk about out-side, or is that not allowed when I'm unaccompanied?'

'Good gracious, child!' the older woman said in sur-prise. 'You're free to walk where you please as long as you don't try to leave the farm.'

'Where are we exactly? What's the nearest town?'

Emma Bryce made no effort now to hide the humour in her glance. 'Bosmansvlei is the nearest town, and if you're thinking of walking there, it's thirty kilometres away.'

Samantha assured her that, for the time being, she felt no desire to overtax her strength by attempting such a lengthy walk in an effort to escape. She refrained from mentioning, however, that she had every inten-tion of investigating every avenue of escape available to her.

There appeared to be no one about when she stepped into the brilliant afternoon sunlight. For a while she strolled aimlessly across the well-kept lawns until she noticed a building to the back of the house which ob-viously housed the farm vehicles as well as those for private use. Endeavouring to appear as casual as pos-sible, she continued her stroll in that direction, intent on invesigating the possibility of making use of one of the estate cars. There was parking space for approxi-mately twelve cars, but only three of the parking bays were occupied. The gleaming white Mercedes was ob-viously Brett's, and the unpretentious Mini—a smile plucked at her lips—could only belong to Emma Bryce, for Brett would never manage to seat his large frame comfortably in such a confined space. The only other vehicle in the garage was a Land-Rover which was being repaired, judging by the various assortment of tools ly-ing about and the amount of grease on the hands of the Coloured man who kept emerging from the interior of the engine to select whichever implement he needed.

It would not be difficult to escape at night if she could make use of one of those cars, but it would be to her disadvantage if she planned too hastily. It would take a little time to discover where the keys were kept, for any direct questions in that respect might cause suspicion and inevitable failure.

The thundering of a horse's hooves interrupted her thoughts and she turned to see horse and rider approaching her across the yard. It was Brett, looking alarmingly different in jodhpurs and khaki bush jacket, with a broad-rimmed slouch hat pulled firmly over his eyes. He drew the horse in beside her and Samantha stepped back swiftly as the temperamental white stallion pawed the air.

'Do you ride?' he asked abruptly, looking down at her with a sardonic expression on his face as he kept a tight hold on the reins to control the horse.

'N-no.'

'Then I shall have to teach you.' To her horror he leaned down towards her and extended his hand. 'Give me your hand and I'll help you up and give you a taste of what it's like.'

'Oh, no!' There was nothing she wanted less at that moment than to get on the back of that vicious-looking animal with Brett.

'Come.' It was a command and she found herself obeying involuntarily. 'Put your left foot in the stirrup and I'll do the rest.'

The quivering animal turned large brown eyes in her direction but remained perfectly still at Brett's command. Samantha did as she was told and quite suddenly found herself sitting on the animal's back with Brett's strong arm about her waist.

'Just as well you're wearing slacks,' he mocked as she

drew her breath in sharply. 'Are you comfortable?'

'Y-yes, thank you,' she managed breathlessly, only too aware of his solid broad chest against her shoulder and the warmth of his muscular arm about her waist. There was about him the smell of the sun which made him almost a complete stranger to her, compared to the immaculately groomed business man she had come to know since that night she had walked into his private garden at the hotel.

She had not been sure what to expect after being hoisted up on to his horse, but she gradually relaxed as she became accustomed to the rhythm of the animal beneath her. Brett's warm breath was against her cheek as they thundered across the veld with its thorn bushes and windmills standing out like beacons, but he did not speak until the horse had slowed its pace to a rhythmic canter.

'Have you ever been on a sheep farm before?' he asked eventually, his voice low and pleasant against her ear.

'Only once when I was a child, but I don't remember much about it,' she owned, allowing her gaze to wander in the direction of the camps where the sheep were grazing lazily. 'Tell me something about it.'

'Are you merely being polite, or do you really want to know?' he asked mockingly, and Samantha felt the tightening of the muscles in his arm.

'I wouldn't ask if I wasn't interested.'

Brett appeared to consider this for a moment, then he laughed softly beneath his breath. 'There's a lot I still have to learn about you, little Samantha.'

'Don't call me that!' she snapped irritably, leaning back slightly to glance up at him and wishing she had not allowed herself to be forced into undertaking this unusual expedition with him.

'What?' he laughed mockingly, strong white teeth flashing against the tan of his skin. 'Little Samantha? You live up to your name, my dear, but what you lack in height you certainly make up for in temperament.'

'I did ask you to tell me something about the farm,' she reminded him coldly, changing the subject swiftly before she lost her temper.

'Your servant, madam,' he mocked thumbing his hat on to the back of his head. 'The grazing area has been fenced off into camps and we graze them in rotation to preserve the natural vegetation. It sounds complicated, but it's really very simple,' he smiled at her when she looked up at him with raised eyebrows, but he continued his explanation without a trace of mockery. 'The lambs are born in spring or at the onset of autumn, but preferably in the spring, as our winters here can be cruel at times.'

The stallion continued its rhythmic walk along the jackal fencing and although Samantha realised that she would suffer some discomfort later as a result of this ride, she was strongly aware of the peacefulness of the country as the late afternoon sun lay warm against her bare arms. In a camp some distance away, two farmhands were herding a large number of lambs into a stone *kraal* and their bleating could be heard clearly across the stillness of the open veld.

'Those lambs have been weaned,' Brett explained, sensing her query. 'They were born during October and are now almost four months old.'

'Do you do your own shearing, or do you enlist the aid of people specially trained to do this?'

'My farmhands do the shearing and sorting themselves,' he said abruptly. 'They're a highly specialised bunch, but the shearing is done only after the winter, from August to October.' He turned the horse sharply and she sucked her breath in sharply as they galloped across the veld, away from the enclosed camps. 'There's someone I want you to meet,' he shouted above the noise of thundering hooves and the wind in her ears.

The Coloured settlement lay beyond a small *kopje*, its neat brick houses shaded by tall bluegum trees. The children were the first to notice them and they ceased their games to greet Brett exuberantly, running alongside the horse as he slowed its pace to a walk and scrambling for the handful of cents he had dropped in the sand. Samantha's presence caused a slight stir among them, but they obviously took it for granted that if she was with Brett she had every right to be there.

Samantha somehow managed to restrain herself from questioning Brett until he slid off his horse at the furthest end of the settlement and placed his hands about her waist to help her down.

'I'm taking you to meet Rosa,' he answered her query, his hands lingering disturbingly at her waist. 'She sent a message via her grandson that I was to bring you to her, and even I don't ignore such a command.'

'But why?' she asked, somewhat surprised. 'She doesn't even know me.'

Brett's lips twitched slightly. 'I think I should warn you. Rosa is rather strange in some ways. She ... sees things, as they say, but she's really quite harmless.'

Samantha shivered involuntarily. 'You make her sound rather frightening.'

'There's nothing frightening about Rosa,' Brett assured her. 'My grandmother died shortly after my father was born, and Rosa looked after him from when he was a baby right through to his adolescence. She's merely a wise old woman with peculiar ways, but don't let her upset you in any way.'

He took her arm and led her towards the cottage built a little distance from the others. The gate opened noiselessly beneath his hand and they walked in silence up the garden path towards the front door. It was opened by a young Coloured woman before Brett could raise his hand to knock and she smiled broadly, gesturing that they should enter. The neat but sparsely furnished room served as a lounge and dining-room, and in a chair beside the scrubbed wooden table sat an old woman, her face lined with age and snow-white hair combed back from her face with a neat plait coiled in her neck. She smiled, displaying teeth that were yellowed with age, and invited them to sit down.

'Rosa, you're an old rogue,' Brett rebuked her kindly once they were seated. 'You're the only person who would have the cheek to order me about.'

'Your father was like my own child,' her voice crackled, 'and you are his son. Your father and your mother are no longer here to look after your welfare, God rest their souls, so I must do the best I can, even if it means ordering you about.'

'You know you're always forgiven,' Brett replied with surprising gentleness.

The old woman nodded and turned dark, beady eyes on Samantha. 'I knew that one day you would come, and when I saw a star shoot in the east last night, I knew that before the sun set on another day, you would be here.'

Samantha glanced nervously at Brett seated beside her, and the look he gave her said clearly: 'What did I tell you?'

'Your name is Samantha,' the old woman continued, and Samantha felt the blood recede from her face. 'I had to see you to tell you what I saw. I'm getting old, you see,' she chuckled with mirth, 'and sometimes I forget things—important things.'

Samantha could not pretend that she was unaffected by Rosa's meanderings and, ignoring the mockery in Brett's glance, she questioned the old woman. 'What is it that's of such importance that you had to tell me?'

Rosa's glance never left Samantha's and she had the most peculiar feeling that the woman was almost sinking into a trance. Her skin crawled. It was almost like delving into the supernatural, something she had heard of and had scoffed at in the past.

'Beware of stardust. It blinds the eye and slips through your fingers,' Rosa's crackling voice interrupted the tense silence. 'When the young leaves of spring sit on the trees you will find your star of happiness.'

Rosa sagged in her chair and bowed her head, clearly exhausted by the effort. Brett drew Samantha to her feet and gestured to the younger woman hovering in the doorway that they were leaving.

'Tell Rosa that Miss Samantha appreciated her concern and that we'll come again some other time,' Brett told the girl, before he marched Samantha firmly from the cottage.

It had been a weird experience that left her mind in a turmoil during the silent ride home. What could the old woman have meant? *Beware of stardust. It blinds the eye and slips through your fingers.* And then there was something about finding her star of happiness in the spring. Was the old woman implying that her happiness with Clive would not materialise before the spring? But that was seven months away, and she had no intention of being parted from Clive for that long!

Brett was strangely distant when they parted company some time later, and during dinner that evening she was aware of his long searching glances. After coffee had been served in the living-room she escaped into the garden to enjoy the peaceful silence of the night. She had to be alone. She had to think!

'There's nothing more brilliant than the stars in the country,' Brett remarked behind her, and she stiffened instantly. 'Have you noticed?'

'I didn't come out here to do stargazing,' she replied, moving away from him along the stoep.

'I did warn you not to take Rosa's ramblings too seriously,' he said drily, almost as though he had read her thoughts.

Samantha turned to face him in the shadowy moonlight. 'You know her better than I do. What was she trying to say?'

The silence was filled with the fragrance of honeysuckle as she waited for him to reply, but he merely shrugged his shoulders carelessly and said: 'I'm afraid I have no idea what she meant.'

'Surely you must have some idea?'

'My dear Samantha,' Brett laughed mockingly, 'how should I know all that goes on in the mind of someone like Rosa? It could have meant that you're chasing after moonbeams, or something equally ridiculous.'

'Now we're back to Clive,' she snapped angrily.

'No, my dear, we're back to you,' Brett corrected, taking her hands in his and drawing her relentlessly towards him in the silvery darkness. 'Marry me, Samantha, and all my worldly goods will be yours.'

'I'm not for sale!' she exclaimed breathlessly, struggling vainly to free her hands and still the clamouring of her heart.

His grip tightened painfully on her wrists. 'If I'd wanted to buy a wife, I could have done so years ago. I'm asking you to be my wife, Samantha.'

'I can't marry you,' she choked out the words. 'I don't love you.'

'Love?' he laughed mockingly, his cool breath against her forehead. 'What is love? You talk of it as if you know, and yet I'm certain that you haven't the faintest idea what it's all about.'

'Let me go! You can't force me to accept by using brute strength,' she panted wildly, but, instead of releasing her, Brett held her firmly against the hard length of his body.

'I agree, Samantha, but I will nevertheless prove to you that you're not as indifferent to me as you would like me to think.'

His mouth was hard against her own, forcing her lips apart and sending a charge of electricity along her nerves. She trembled, struggled to subdue her rising emotions, and finally knew that, subconsciously, she had wanted him to kiss her in this way. Horrified and ashamed of herself, she broke free, and Brett made no effort to stop her. It was anger that came to her rescue, or she might have burst into tears as she stood facing him on that still summer night with her fickle heart hammering against her ribs.

'Am I to be subjected to this kind of treatment throughout my enforced stay?' she gasped, trying to control the trembling of her hands by clasping them behind her back. 'Do you intend to wear down my defences until I no longer have the will to refuse?'

The silence was heavily charged as they faced each other. Brett's expression was formidable in the moonlight, and Samantha's nerves twisted into a tight coil.

'You must allow me to know what's best for you,' he said with surprising calmness. 'You have my word that I shan't kiss you again unless you give some sign that you wish it, but I will not discontinue my efforts to make you accept my proposal of marriage.'

'You'll be wasting your time!'

'I think not, Samantha,' he contradicted harshly. 'I'm a patient man. I can wait.'

'You'll wait for ever, Brett Carrington!' she flung at him, her cheeks burning with humiliation and anger as she made her escape while his mocking laughter followed her until she had entered the house.

The living-room was empty, but Emma Bryce met her in the hall, her manner less disapproving and an unmistakable warmth in her grey eyes. 'I've taken the liberty of selecting a few things from Nadine's wardrobe for you to choose from. You'll find them in your room.'

'Thank you very much, Mrs Bryce. I think if you don't mind, I would like to retire to my room. It's been rather a tiring day.'

'Of course, my dear,' she nodded understandingly, 'and call me Aunt Emma. Everyone does.'

There was a genuine warmth in her voice that brought swift tears to Samantha's eyes as she stammered her thanks. 'You're very kind, and it would make me very happy to call you Aunt Emma.'

They could hear Brett closing the doors leading on to the stoep and, noticing Samantha's nervous glance in that direction, the older woman gave her a gentle push towards the stairs. 'Off to bed with you. You've had enough for one day.'

Samantha smiled at her gratefully and fled upstairs, not stopping until she reached the privacy of her room. Aunt Emma was right, she *had* had enough for one day. Enough of Brett's arrogance and mockery, enough bitterness and anger, and enough disappointment at her father and Gillian's contribution to her unhappiness.

Later, dressed in the frilly lace nightgown which had

been laid out for her, Samantha lay staring into the darkness, nursing the unfamiliar stiffness that was setting in from her ride and with a mind too exhausted to think as she watched the moon spread its soft glow across her bed. Too much had happened, and all of it disturbing. Beware of stardust, Rosa had said. Was it merely the ramblings of an old woman, or did it have some hidden meaning? she wondered, sighing heavily.

There was nothing as blissfully silent as the Karoo nights, and nothing more soothing for a mind bruised by tortuous thoughts. Samantha closed her eyes in these unfamiliar surroundings and allowed the silence to wash over her, lulling her into a false state of serenity until she drifted into the oblivion of sleep.

CHAPTER SIX

BRETT left the homestead soon after breakfast the following morning, but arrived back in time to have tea with Aunt Emma and herself on the stoep, and Samantha could not prevent the flicker of admiration that passed through her as she glanced at him surreptitiously. Despite the fact that he was wearing khaki drill trousers and bush jacket, he looked as immaculate as always, and somehow such a part of this vast semi-desert country.

'Would you like to come for a swim with me?' he asked, wiping the perspiration from his brow with a spotless handkerchief. 'There's a natural pool in the *vlei* that we always use for this purpose.'

'You're forgetting I've brought nothing with me, and that my clothes haven't arrived yet,' she reminded him coolly.

'I dare say I could rustle up a swimsuit for you,' he said drily before disappearing into the house.

Aunt Emma shrugged her shoulders at Samantha's doubtful glance and removed the tray to the kitchen while Samantha followed Brett upstairs with some trepidation. There was no knowing what he would 'rustle up' as he had put it, and she was beginning to wonder if it would not have been wiser to decline his invitation.

Brett met her at the top of the stairs, a towel hanging about his neck. 'I've left something in your room for you. I'll be waiting out at the back for you, so come down when you're ready.'

He disappeared down the stairs and Samantha turned warily towards her room.

The 'something' he had mentioned turned out to be the minutest dark green bikini she had ever seen, and she blushed crimson just looking at herself in the mirror. If it had not been so suffocatingly hot, and the thought of a swim so tempting, she would have thought twice about wearing the scanty garment Brett had found for her. It was perhaps also some of Gillian's devilment that had rubbed off on her over the years that prevented her from shying away from the idea of appearing like that before Brett. She might be short, she thought, surveying herself in the mirror, but her figure was good. Her breasts were small and firm, her waist slender, her hips rounded perfectly, and her legs shapely. There was nothing Brett could find fault with. As if she cared, she added to herself defiantly.

She found a pair of denim slacks in the cupboard which she had to roll up round her ankles, and a brightly coloured blouse which she left hanging loosely over her belt. In a hurry now not to keep Brett waiting, she slipped on her shoes and grabbed a towel before hurrying down the stairs and out to the back.

'Over here!' Brett called as she emerged from the house, and she glanced across to see him standing beneath the old oak tree holding on to the reins of his own magnificent white stallion as well as a grey mare. 'If you're going to learn to ride, then you might as well start now.'

'Brett, I can't!' she exclaimed, her throat tightening with fear as she came forward hesitantly.

'Coward!'

This was too much! She could take Brett's mockery, but she was not a coward, and she steeled herself to stretch out a hand and stroke the mare's neck. It was a pleasant sensation to feel the smooth coat beneath her fingers.

'What's her name?'

'I call her Meisie—Girl,' he translated for her haughtily.

'I can understand Afrikaans,' she informed him, meeting his glance with a shade of anger in her eyes. 'Don't treat me as though I were illiterate!'

'Don't be so touchy,' he rebuked her, lifting her into the saddle as if she were no weight at all. 'Meisie is very tame, so you have nothing to fear. Just do as I tell you and soon you'll be riding like an expert.'

'Brett,' she began with rising panic, 'what if I fall off?'

'My dear child,' he laughed mockingly, 'no one has ever fallen off Meisie, so stop imagining all sorts of mishaps and do exactly as I tell you.'

It was a nerve-racking ride down to the *vlei*, but it was fun. Under Brett's firm guidance she soon began to feel secure as she watched her movements to the rhythm of the mare, while her muscles objected to this unaccustomed exercise.

'Relax your hold on the reins slightly,' Brett instructed at one stage. 'You've got her pulling at the bit and it can hurt her mouth. That's better.'

Samantha knew that she would never forget that unusual but pleasant smell of leather and horseflesh, combined with the spiky odour of the veld. It was an experience she would not have exchanged for anything else in the world at that moment—riding with Brett in the hot Karoo sun, and seeing a side of him few others knew of. This was his kingdom; it was where he belonged, and not in the harsh businesslike world where she had met him and once thought him such a part of.

'We're almost there,' he interrupted her thoughts,

and she glanced in the direction he was pointing to see a shady pool, protected from the glare of the sun by the willow trees growing on its banks.

Brett dismounted first and helped her down before tethering the horses to a tree. They stripped down to their costumes and Samantha turned warily to follow Brett into the water, only to find that he appeared in no hurry to enjoy the coolness of the pool. He stood there with a male arrogance that was both disarming and infuriating, his glance moving down the length of her with a slow deliberation that quickened her pulse and sent the blood drumming in her ears. She was painfully aware of the fact that the bikini he had given her left very little to the imagination, and her cheeks went hot with embarrassment.

Unable to endure his prolonged scrutiny, she turned and plunged into the cool, refreshing water, but she was surprised to find Brett surfacing beside her almost simultaneously. His hair was plastered to his head and there was a wicked look in his dark eyes.

'Be careful,' he warned mockingly. 'That bikini wasn't made to take rough treatment.'

'Go away!' she cried in an anguish of embarrassment, striking out towards the opposite bank. But Brett caught up with her, his arm heavy about her waist as he dragged her against him, and she automatically clutched at those broad shoulders.

'Teasing time is over,' he said severely. 'Don't swim that way, it's dangerously deep. Keep to this side of the pool.'

He released her then and Samantha obeyed him without resentment, swimming only where he had indicated it was safe. She rolled over on to her back and floated, watching the dragonflies hovering like helicopters above the water.

'Do you often swim here?' she asked when he reached her side once more, treading water.

'Almost every day in the summer,' he replied with a gleam of mockery in his eyes. 'But I don't usually swim in this respectable fashion.'

'What do you mean?'

His amusement deepened at her innocence. 'I swim in the nude. A costume is something I don't normally carry around with me.'

Samantha blushed profusely and, avoiding his glance, she swam out to the side of the pool.

'We'd better dry off in the sun before we change back into our clothes,' he suggested, following her out and towelling himself vigorously.

Samantha spread out her towel on the grass and sat down, her hands clasped about her knees, her hair wet and stringy, sending rivulets of water down her back and making her shiver in the sun.

'I have something for you,' Brett said, seating himself beside her with his smooth shoulder almost touching hers.

She took the square envelope from him and recognised her father's handwriting immediately. 'You must have had this with you since yesterday. Why are you only giving it to me now?'

'You weren't in a very understanding mood yesterday, so I withheld it a little.'

Samantha bit back a sharp retort and tore open the envelope, extracting a single sheet of paper with her father's neat handwriting on it.

'My dear Samantha,' he had written, 'This is not an easy letter to write, because I know how you must be hating me at this moment. It was not an easy decision for me to take. Tricking one's own daughter into a situation she doesn't desire is never very pleasant, but you wouldn't have gone willingly.

'Perhaps you will forgive me when I tell you that I've longed to get away from Port Elizabeth and the aching memories of the happiness your mother and I had shared. I couldn't force you to come with me to Cape Town, and I couldn't leave you behind with someone like Clive Wilmot in the offing. That's why, when Brett suggested an unscheduled visit to his farm where you would be under his care and that of his aunt's, I jumped at the chance.

'Think of it as a holiday, Samantha, and the opportunity to make sure of your feelings for Clive. If he loves you as he says he does, he'll wait for you. As Brett put it to me: something worthwhile is always worth waiting for.

'Don't judge me too harshly, my dear, and write to me when you have the time. Your loving father, James Little.'

She felt the tears prick her eyelids as she returned the letter to the envelope. Brett had moved away from her and stood leaning against a tree, smoking a cigarette and staring out across the water with an almost brooding expression on his face.

Samantha lay down on her back and felt the sting of the sun against her closed eyelids. She could almost forgive her father, and yet ... Brett's shadow fell across her and as she raised her glance she found herself trapped by those peculiar gold-flecked eyes, a clear blue sky, and the gently swaying branches of the willow trees.

'Why, Brett?' she demanded, catching her trembling lower lip between her teeth. 'Why am I not free to live my life as I wish, and to love whom I please?'

Brett's expression remained unchanged except for a

slight tightening of his lips. 'You haven't loved yet, Samantha, but you will one day—the right man.'

She had an idea that they were not talking about the same thing, but she let it pass and did not mention the subject again as they dressed and rode back to the homestead.

Brett's chauffeur-driven black Mercedes arrived that afternoon with Samantha's suitcases, and it was only when they stood in a neat row at the foot of her bed that the stark reality of her predicament took its toll on her nerves. She wept, washed her face and wept again. She was being silly, she told herself. She was not normally the weepy kind, but she found that she was incapable of stemming the flow of tears.

Her first week at Carrington's Post dragged by, but during this time she quelled her impatience and spent her time planning a way of escape. Brett seldom left her alone, taking her with him through acres of grazing paddocks, or down to the *vlei* for a swim in the pool; he on his white stallion, Lightning, and she on Meisie. Although he kept his word and did not try to kiss her again, Samantha became so aware of him as a forceful and virile man that she wondered which was worse; being kissed by him, or being so alarmingly aware of him.

Despite the rocky start, Emma Bryce became her friend, but Samantha knew instinctively that she could not share her confidences with this woman, for her loyalty to Brett outweighed their friendship. If Emma Bryce knew of her plans she would inform her nephew instantly.

Samantha soon discovered that the keys to all the vehicles were kept in Brett's book-lined study. It was a comfortable, businesslike room with padded leather chairs and a heavy mahogany desk. She had been in there once with Brett when Lucas happened to return the keys of the Land-Rover and she had seen Lucas hang them on a hook in a small unlocked cupboard behind the door. She would have to bide her time, she decided. Brett must not suspect that she had intentions of making a bid for freedom. Freedom—a strange word, but an apt one. She was imprisoned by Brett as a man, and by her own unpredictable emotions. She had to get away—to escape from thoughts and feelings brought on by his dominating presence.

Her opportunity came one evening during her second week at the farm. Brett announced at dinner that he would be attending a meeting in the district that evening. That left Aunt Emma and Samantha completely alone. Aunt Emma normally went to bed early and that would mean that Samantha would be free to collect the keys of the Mercedes and make her escape before Brett returned. It was all too ridiculously easy, she thought humorously. If Brett intended to keep her a prisoner, then he would have to keep her chained like a slave.

'Goodnight, Samantha,' Brett bowed mockingly as he was on his way out. 'Forgive me for robbing you of my charming company this evening.'

'Your company won't be missed, I assure you,' she replied with sarcasm. It was her only weapon against his mockery and she was forced to use it frequently.

'The day will come, my dear,' Brett continued unperturbed, 'when you'll long for my company ... and plenty more besides.'

Samantha flushed deeply but did not avert her gaze. 'Don't be too sure of yourself, Brett Carrington. Not all women are prepared to fall at your feet when you happen to beckon. Some may find you irresistible, but to me you're rather an arrogant bore.'

Brett went white about the mouth and Aunt Emma, who had been listening to this verbal battle in silence, drew her breath in sharply. Samantha waited, not knowing what to expect, but Brett recovered swiftly and ordered Aunt Emma to leave them alone for a brief moment.

'Don't try me too far, Samantha,' he said harshly as the door closed behind his aunt, 'or I might forget my promise to you and show you just how irresistible you do find me.'

Samantha took an involuntary step backwards, her pulse drumming in her ears. 'I hate you, Brett!'

'Good,' he snapped, his eyes like two coals of fire in his head. 'If you can love as vehemently as you hate, then being married to you will be an enthralling revelation.'

She placed her hands against her burning cheeks as he turned on his heel and left the room. He was an infuriated, self-opinionated, hateful man, and she would *never* marry him. Never!

The outer door slammed behind him and moments later Aunt Emma re-entered the living-room.

'Was that Brett I heard leaving?' she asked, taking in Samantha's flaming cheeks and blue eyes now almost black with anger.

'Yes.'

'My dear, you must be careful,' she said with deep concern. 'Brett is very much accustomed to having his own way and he doesn't tolerate people speaking to him the way you do.'

Samantha's eyes stung with angry tears. 'I did not mean to be disrespectful, but why must he always mock and taunt me the way he does?'

Emma Bryce shook her head and slipped a comforting arm about Samantha's shoulders. 'I don't know what's got into Brett lately. He's not usually like this. He's really a very kind and considerate man, firm with those who work for him, but never cruel.'

Samantha swallowed at the lump in her throat and quelled her sudden desperate longing for the comforting warmth of Clive's arms, and the firm assurance that he loved her. If her plan worked, she would soon be with him and no one, not even Brett Carrington, would succeed in taking her away from him a second time.

'I think I'll have an early night,' she told the older woman, and dropped a light kiss on her cheek before going up to her room.

It was not long before she heard footsteps passing her door. Aunt Emma was retiring for the night and within half an hour her light would be out. She would give her an hour before making her first move, just to make sure that she would be asleep.

The hour seemed to drag by as Samantha waited, her two suitcases side by side at the door, and her nerves twisted into a tangled knot. The worst part, she discovered later, was tiptoeing down the darkened stairs, collecting the keys from Brett's study, and slipping from the house without waking Aunt Emma. Once outside, she kept to the shadows and reached the garages without much difficulty. The black Mercedes was not in its usual place, but the white Mercedes looked inviting in the moonlight. It would perhaps have been better to take Aunt Emma's Mini, but once she was on the main road beyond Bosmansvlei she would need speed to get away as quickly as possible.

She placed her suitcases in the boot and slipped into the driver's seat. She was practically on her way, she thought, her hands trembling with excitement. Nothing could stop her now. She turned the key in the igni-

tion and pressed the starter. Nothing happened! She
tried again ... and still nothing happened. She flicked
the switch for the lights but, when they did not come
on, she realised with a sickening jolt that the battery
must have been removed. Her suspicions were confirmed when, moments later, she had the bonnet open.
She hurried across to the Mini and, to her chagrin,
found that it was also without a battery.

'Having trouble, Samantha?'

'Brett!' Her heart leapt to her throat with a violence
that almost choked her as she swung round to face the
tall, menacing figure approaching her in the darkness.

'I had an idea you were planning something like
this,' he told her with a calmness that frightened her.
'That's why I invented the meeting and deliberately
gave you the opportunity.'

Samantha's limbs were numb with shock. 'You mean
... you've been here all the time?'

'Yes, I parked the car further along among the trees
and waited.' He seemed to tower over her trembling
form. 'I must admit I never thought you'd have the
nerve to try.'

Samantha was too numb to speak and she leaned
weakly against the bonnet of the car while he removed
her suitcases from the boot and slipped the keys into
his pocket. He gestured that she should follow him and
she did so meekly, her legs trembling to such an extent
that she stumbled several times in the darkness from
the garages to the house. When they reached his study
he stood aside for her to enter and then closed the door
behind them with his foot before dropping her suitcases on to the floor.

She sat down thankfully in the first available chair
and clasped her trembling hands in her lap. Her body
quivered uncontrollably and her teeth were clamped

so tightly together that her jaw ached.

'Drink this,' Brett spoke beside her, a glass of amber-coloured liquid in his hand.

She could hardly hold the glass properly and some of the liquid splashed on to her slacks. 'What is it?'

'Brandy and water,' he said abruptly. 'It will steady your nerves. You're shaking like a leaf.'

'I can't drink it!' she protested through clenched teeth, but the look in his eyes made any further protestations die on her lips. She coughed and spluttered as the first mouthful scalded her throat, but he forced the glass to her lips once more. She obediently took another mouthful before pressing the glass into his hand. 'Please, I've had enough. It's quite revolting!'

She leaned back in her chair, closing her eyes as she felt the welcome warmth steal through her veins and finally steadying her quivering nerves. What was Brett going to do? she wondered suddenly, glancing at his impassive face from beneath her eyelashes. She had expected him to be angered, but this calm acceptance he was displaying made it difficult for her to know just how to handle the situation.

'While making your plans of escape, Samantha, did you give a thought to where you would go?' he asked suddenly, leaning against his desk and folding his arms across his chest.

'Well, I obviously can't go back to the flat, as it's been let to someone else, I presume.' She avoided the directness of his gaze. 'I'll find a room somewhere.'

'Or you could move in with Wilmot.'

'That's a vile thing to say!' she flared hotly, gripping the arms of her chair. 'What do you think I am?'

Brett raised his eyebrows mockingly. 'You're not going to tell me he's never suggested it?'

'Of course not! He ...' She bit her lip suddenly, recalling an incident she would have preferred to forget. Clive had insisted that there was no reason for them not not to live together until his salary could provide adequately for a wife, and she had refused adamantly. Now, with Brett waiting patiently for her to reply, she was forced to admit the truth. 'Yes.'

'Well, then?' he persisted cynically.

'I'm old-fashioned enough to believe that that sort of thing is for after the marriage.' She felt the tell-tale colour seeping into her cheeks, but she faced him with a touch of defiance. 'Am I going to be punished for trying to get away?'

'Yes.'

He took her hands and drew her to her feet, and quite suddenly she knew what he intended to do. She could have freed herself quite easily, for he did not take her into his arms, but for some unaccountable reason she remained perfectly still as he lowered his head. His lips moved over hers in a lingering kiss that made her tremble, and when his unusual chastisement finally ended, her eyes, deep blue and questioning, held his glance.

'Is that all?' she heard herself asking almost with a sigh.

'Am I to believe you're asking for more, Samantha?'

'You know very well what I mean,' she bit out, furious with herself for inviting his mockery. 'The least I expected was a lashing with your tongue, if not with a whip.'

'I'm not a barbarian to take a whip to a woman, or anyone else for that matter,' he stated harshly, releasing her hands and taking a pace away from her to allow his glance to slide over the length of her. 'There are other forms of punishment which are far more effective.'

Samantha's cheeks stung with humiliation, but fortunately Brett's back was turned towards her as he collected her suitcases. It was a silent, agonising walk up to her room, with Brett, cold and forbidding, directly behind her. He placed her suitcases just inside the door and then looked down at her disdainfully from his great height.

'Goodnight, Samantha.'

She stammered something, but he was gone before the words had formed properly on her lips. Disappointed and despondent, she bit back the tears. If only she could accept her father's explanation for agreeing that Brett should practically abduct her and keep her a prisoner. What right had they to interfere? If Clive was not the kind of man her father had had in mind for her, then surely he should have had the grace to accept the fact that she had made her choice, and that she was old enough to know what she wanted? Or was it merely that Brett's suggestion had been the easy way out for him, leaving him free to accept the transfer he had secretly desired since her mother's untimely death? she wondered unhappily. She had heard of parents objecting to their children's chosen escorts, but *this* was more than ridiculous and totally unreasonable.

Her thoughts returned to Clive, and the most unnerving realisation swept through her. It was not so much Clive whom she wanted to rush *to*, but Brett she wanted to escape *from*. But what was she running from? An awareness; a sensing of danger? Was she afraid of allowing herself to become submerged in a whirlpool of emotions as yet unexplored by herself? Or was it perhaps the knowledge that Brett could awaken these emotions, where Clive had failed in the past?

A shuddering sigh escaped her and she instantly shied away from these disturbing thoughts as she prepared for bed. It would perhaps be advisable not to delve too deeply into her reasons for wanting to get away from Carrington's Post, she decided tiredly, snapping off the light and acknowledging temporary defeat.

Samantha was more determined than ever now to get away. At the first available opportunity to speak to Lucas without Brett breathing down her neck, she tried to persuade him to place one of the cars at her disposal, but Lucas could not be swayed.

'Miss Samantha,' he said in that peculiarly accented voice attributed only to the Coloured people, 'my family have lived on this farm for many years, and this is where I want to live until I die.'

Samantha could not prevent the smile that tugged at her lips. 'Does this mean that you won't help me?'

'It means, Miss Samantha,' he replied, his expression apologetic, 'that I can't help you even if I wanted to. Master Brett gave his orders.'

'Do you always obey your boss so implicitly?'

Lucas' eyes widened in his brown face. 'Miss Samantha, if Master Brett said I must chop off my arm, I will chop it off.'

Samantha swallowed her disappointment. 'Your loyalty is commendable, Lucas. Forgive me for asking you to go against your boss's wishes, and forget that I ever asked you to consider doing so.'

Lucas smiled with relief and touched his hat respectfully before leaving her to contemplate the only other avenue of escape left open to her. She would have to get away from the house before dawn one morning and make her way on foot to the road before the heat of the day made such a feat impossible. If she managed to get a lift into Bosmansvlei, she could take a train from there to Port Elizabeth.

It was three days before Samantha could put this plan into action. For two days it rained incessantly and on the third Brett kept her busy in his study, dictating letters which he had asked her to type. Her elation was almost impossible to bear when she eventually found herself on the road to Bosmansvlei at the first light of dawn with a change of clothing in her small vanity case, as well as her savings book and enough cash in her sling bag to pay for a train ticket. The rest of her possessions would just have to remain at Carrington's Post to be collected later.

Samantha walked at an easy pace, the wild smell of the Karoo bush permeating the air. It would be two hours before her disappearance would be noticed and that would give her more than enough time to get as far away as possible. By seven that morning the sun had dispersed the chill of early dawn, and the glistening dew drops on the grass and scrubs transformed the veld into a twinkling paradise.

Several cars had passed her, going in the opposite direction, and she was close to giving up hope when she heard a car approaching from behind. She turned to thumb a lift but never completed the action, for the car approaching her was Brett's. He drew up alongside her and climbed out with those leisurely, panther-like movements that so often had held her spellbound, and came towards her, his thumbs tucked into the belt of his immaculate grey trousers.

'Going somewhere?'

Samantha swallowed violently at the constriction in her throat when she met the cold fury of his glance.

'Brett, I——'

'Get in!' he thundered, wrenching open the door on the passenger side and helping her forcibly into the seat.

With pounding temples she waited for him to get in beside her and turn the car round. An ominous silence lingered between them during the drive back to Carrington's Post, where he pulled her roughly from the car and marched her into the house and directly to his study.

'Brett, you can't keep me a prisoner here on your farm,' she began bravely despite the chill of fear that curled along her spine. 'If I went to the police I could have you arrested.'

Brett laughed harshly as he faced her across his desk. 'My dear child, you're here as my guest and, what's more, I have in my possession a letter signed by your father in which he assigned you to my guardianship until you reach the age of twenty-one.'

'I don't believe you!'

Brett unlocked the drawer of his desk with a savage movement and pushed a piece of paper towards her. 'Take a look at that. It's a photostat copy of the original.'

Samantha's throat tightened, virtually choking off her breath as she read through the letter and discovered that Brett had spoken the truth. 'So I've been tricked and trapped with the help of my own father ... the one person I've always thought I could trust implicitly!'

'Don't say that!' He came round his desk with a few quick strides and gripped her shoulders painfully. 'If you weren't so stubborn you would realise that your father has your welfare at heart, just as I do.'

'Why?' her voice croaked as his face swam before her. 'Why should you care what happens to me?'

'You're too lovely to have your life ruined by a cad like Clive Wilmot.'

'You don't know Clive!' she protested, her lips quivering as she voiced the habitual complaint.

'Don't I?' Brett released her and lit a cigarette, blowing the smoke forcefully into the air. 'Samantha, if I bring you positive proof that Clive has not been faithful to you ... will you marry me?'

She clenched her hands at her sides. 'That's unfair!'

'If you're as sure of Clive as you say you are, then what have you to lose?' he challenged, his eyes watchful, his mouth twisting cynically.

'Very well,' she agreed in angry defiance and with a confidence that was showing signs of crumbling. 'But you won't find any such proof.'

'We shall see,' he mocked. 'Meanwhile, do you also give me your word that you'll remain here if I fly to Port Elizabeth this morning in order to obtain this proof?'

'You have my word that I'll remain here, but ... if you don't find the proof you seek?' Her blue gaze was raised to his imploringly.

'Then I shall personally return you to Clive.' A look of distaste flashed across his face. 'Do we have a bargain?'

Samantha's heart pounded uncomfortably against her ribs. 'Yes ... but you'll be disappointed.'

CHAPTER SEVEN

THE homestead was ominously quiet after Brett's departure, and Samantha had plenty of time to regret her foolishness in allowing him to trap her into an agreement which could quite easily force her into marrying him. It had been madness; but it was done.

Eventually, when she could bear the silence no longer, she went in search of Aunt Emma and found her in the garden, pottering among the plants with a wide-brimmed hat on her head as protection against the sun.

'Can I help?' she asked, wishing there was something she could do to quell the frightening thoughts that raced madly through her mind.

'Without garden gloves you'll spoil your lovely hands,' Aunt Emma remarked seriously. 'Sit down somewhere and we can talk if you like.'

Samantha sat down on the grass beside the little stream and trailed her fingers in the water. If Aunt Emma knew about her attempt to hitch-hike to Bosmansvlei that morning, then she was diplomatic enough not to mention it, Samantha thought gratefully.

'Tell me about Brett's parents, Aunt Emma.'

The older woman glanced up briefly and smiled. 'There isn't much to tell. Brett's mother died not long after Nadine's birth, and as I was widowed at the time I came back to the farm to look after my brother, Brett's father, and the two children. Brett was fourteen when Nadine was born, and already an indepenent young man with ideas of his own.' She pushed the garden fork into the ground and removed her gloves. 'Of course, with his mother's untimely death, he developed a protective love for Nadine, and actually spoiled her tremendously. It was Brett who taught her to swim and to ride horses ... and to drive that dreadful little red sports car he'd given her on her nineteeth birthday.' Aunt Emma sighed and stared thoughtfully out across the veld to where the tractors were ploughing up the earth to plant lucerne for the winter. 'He blamed himself very much for her death. I think perhaps that's why ...'

'Yes?' Samantha prompted, her interest quickening as Aunt Emma's voice trailed off into a guilty silence.

'Nothing,' she shook her head firmly. 'Let's go back to the house, it's almost time to have tea.'

Samantha slipped her arm through Aunt Emma's as they walked slowly along the path. 'You haven't told me much about Brett's father. What was he like?'

A reminiscent smile hovered about Aunt Emma's lips. 'Brett is very much like his father. He was also tall and dark, but a much gentler man than Brett. He was very much a dreamer, whereas Brett has always had his feet planted firmly on the ground. He died ten years ago after suffering a very bad thrombosis,' she added almost abruptly, but Samantha noticed the film of tears in her eyes and thought it best not to pursue the subject.

Tea was served on the stoep with the usual melt-in-the-mouth jam tarts, but Samantha was too agitated to enjoy them. She eventually left Aunt Emma in the kitchen, supervising lunch, and had Meisie saddled in the hope that a ride in the veld might dispel the awful feeling of dread in her heart, but she returned an hour later feeling slightly worse than when she had started out.

Samantha finally ended up pacing the living-room floor as the lunch hour drew near. Brett had said he would be back before one, with or without the proof he had gone in search of, and, as the time for his return grew near, she became aware of a terrifying anxiety building up within her.

Aunt Emma set aside her embroidery and glanced up at her with concern. 'Samantha ... my dear, aren't you happy here with us? Haven't we done our best to make you settle in comfortably?'

Samantha allowed her gaze to wander out across the sunlit garden and watched the restless progress of a butterfly on the crimson poppies. 'I could be very happy here, if only ...'

'If only the man you loved could be here to share it with you,' Aunt Emma finished for her, nodding understandingly.

Samantha frowned and turned away from the window. 'Aunt Emma, what am I going to do?' she asked hoarsely, and then, without intending to, it all came tumbling out, her words falling over one another as she explained the true reason for Brett's sudden trip to Port Elizabeth.

'Don't you think it was rather foolish of you to enter into such an agreement with Brett?' Aunt Emma asked when she had finished.

'I had no choice. My faith in Clive was challenged, and besides, he won't find the proof he seeks.'

Aunt Emma raised her eyebrows with a touch of unaccustomed cynicism and picked up her embroidery. 'I hope for your sake that you're right.'

Samantha observed for a moment those surprisingly supple fingers as they worked deftly with needle and thread, before she resumed her pacing with renewed energy. What if Brett had succeeded in his mission and returned with proof? She shuddered inwardly as she thought of the result. Surely he would not insist on her honouring their ridiculous agreement?

'For goodness' sake, child! Come and sit down, you're wearing out the carpet,' Aunt Emma exclaimed impatiently.

'I'm sorry,' Samantha muttered, perching nervously on the arm of a nearby chair, but, even as she did so, she heard the distant droning of Brett's plane and jumped swiftly to her feet. 'He's here!'

'Sit down, Samantha,' Aunt Emma instructed firmly. 'You'll have your answer soon enough.'

It seemed an eternity before they heard the Land-Rover come up the drive and seconds later Brett entered the house, tall and broad-shouldered, his tie askew, the top button of his shirt undone, and the jacket of his dark grey suit slung across his arm. Samantha glanced nervously at Aunt Emma before returning her glance to Brett where he stood in the doorway, his face dark with suppressed anger.

'Well . . .' he said harshly, 'you have a choice.'

'A . . . choice?'

'Yes!' He gestured with his briefcase. 'Do you want the results now, or would you prefer to enjoy your lunch first?'

A frightened pulse leapt in her throat. 'I . . . I don't . . .'

'Brett, you're frightening the child,' Aunt Emma intervened swiftly, her glance disapproving, but not without a touch of sympathy for the girl who stood pale and rigid beside her chair.

'My apologies.' He inclined his head mockingly. 'Shall we go to my study and get it over with, Samantha?'

Samantha followed him down the passage and into the austere atmosphere of his study, where she stood facing him with a feeling of renewed dread in her heart. Was this terrible anger in him as a result of the success or failure of his trip? she wondered with growing alarm. It was difficult to tell with Brett, she had come to realise, for his moods altered with terrifying swiftness.

On his desk stood a photograph of Nadine, her features soft and rounded, her dark eyes alight with gentle amusement, and her equally dark hair tumbling down across her shoulder in silken curls. What had sent this lovely girl careering along a mountain pass to crash to her death? she wondered distractedly, looking up to find Brett appraising her thoughtfully.

'Brett, you couldn't have found——' She choked off the words as flames of anger leapt in his eyes.

'I'm afraid I have.'

'I don't believe you!' she cried in despair, fighting to control the tremors that shook through her. 'This is some sort of trick to get me to honour my part of the bargain. Clive would never——'

'Clive has!' he interrupted brutally, opening his briefcase and pressing a wad of photographs into her hands. 'Take a look at that, and check the date, time and place noted at the bottom of each photograph.'

Samantha studied the photographs with an odd sensation at the pit of her stomach. It was as though the floor had given way beneath her feet and she was falling into a bottomless pit. There was a photograph taken of Clive at a night-club with a dark-haired girl, and there was something decidedly intimate about the way he held her. There was another of them entering a block of flats on the beach-front that same evening, wearing the same clothes as in the first photograph, and another of the girl leaving the building the following morning.

'The flat is registered in the name of Mr and Mrs

Clive Wilmot,' she heard Brett say as she dropped the rest of the photographs on to his desk.

'Where—where did you get these?'

'I employed a private detective to follow him during these past weeks.'

She felt physically ill as she faced him, her cheeks deathly pale and a wounded expression in her eyes. 'I think you're despicable! I——'

'I've brought you proof, Samantha. Proof of what Clive Wilmot really is,' Brett interrupted relentlessly. 'Now I shall expect you to keep to your side of the bargain.'

'You're not going to tell me you actually took that ridiculous agreement seriously?'

'Do you want to back out now that you've lost?' he counter-questioned cynically.

'No ... I'll keep to my side of the bargain. I'll marry you, I ...' Her voice faltered as hot tears welled up in her eyes and slid down her cheeks before she could prevent them. 'Nothing ... matters now.'

A spotless white handkerchief was pressed into her hands. 'Clive Wilmot isn't worthy of your tears.'

'You d-don't understand,' she moaned into the white linen, trying unsuccessfully to stem the flow of tears. 'I loved ... loved him.'

He muttered something unintelligible and quite suddenly she found herself in his arms with her head pressed against his shoulder. It was a comforting gesture, so unexpected from him, but he held her quite firmly and dispassionately until her silent weeping ceased.

'I'm sorry,' she managed eventually in a muffled voice, extricating herself from his arms and wiping her face. 'I must look a mess.'

'I think the sooner we're married, the better,' he remarked, and she did not dare look at him. 'I'll contact your father this afternoon and ask formally for your hand in marriage, as well as for the required written permission as you're still under age.'

Samantha felt as though every vestige of feeling had deserted her. 'You're serious, then ... about marrying me?'

'I've never been more serious about anything in my life,' he said with quiet determination as she raised her glance to his.

'Despite the fact that I don't l-love you?'

'Samantha, I believe that marriages founded on the solid basis of truth and respect are far more successful than most others,' he replied mockingly, capturing her trembling hands in his. 'Given time, my dear, we could be as happy as anyone else.'

Alone in her room, with the tray of lunch Brett had had sent up to her still untouched on the small table where the maid had placed it, reaction began to filter through the blanket of numbness like a douche of icy water, setting her nerves tingling and driving her close to panic. She saw again those damning photographs and a searing pain shot through her. Clive had not waited, but within a matter of a few short weeks he had found someone else and had married her. What had happened then to all his arguments that his salary was not sufficient to keep a wife? she wondered miserably, failing to understand his reasoning.

It was obvious to her now that no man could be trusted, she thought with unaccustomed bitterness. She had trusted Clive and, because of that foolish trust, she had allowed herself to be trapped into an agreement with Brett—an agreement she was now forced to honour.

What did it really matter whom she married? Her hopes and girlish dreams had been shattered, and she would never love again. Never! It was agony to love someone, because it brought only immeasurable pain and disillusionment.

Within less than a month, according to what Brett had told his aunt when he called her into his study, they would be married. The thought unnerved her. Marriage to Brett Carrington was something she would never have contemplated under normal circumstances. He was far too arrogant and domineering and, as a husband, would be demanding and exacting, something she would be incapable of coping with. She could never love Brett, but he had not offered her love ... simply marriage. But with marriage there came certain obligations which made her shudder merely to think of it. Would Brett demand that she fulfil her wifely duties, something which he had every right to expect?

She covered her face with her hands as the blood rushed into her cheeks and then receded to leave her deathly pale. There was still time to escape, she thought frantically, before sanity returned to crush the idea before it had even materialised. Whatever else she might be, she was not a coward. The future had to be faced, and she would do so with as much dignity as possible. She would save face by marrying Brett, and in doing so she would be showing Clive that she had emerged from their relationship unscathed. She would not give him the satisfaction of knowing that, because he had failed her, her life lay in ruins about her.

Marriage to Brett would have its compensations. He was extremely wealthy, and as his wife she would have access to that wealth. A strangled moan escaped her as, sickened by her own thoughts, she fell across the bed and buried her face in the pillow. She was tired. Tired of fighting for Clive's non-existent virtues; tired of fighting against Brett's determination to marry her, and most of all, tired of trying to understand the frightening pattern her life had become.

The following three weeks consisted of whirlwind trips to Port Elizabeth to select material for her wedding gown and several fittings before Aunt Emma was satisfied with the results. Brett had made arrangements for them to spend their honeymoon on the island of Mauritius and insisted on depositing a large amount in her bank account with which to buy a suitable trousseau. Simple cottons and linens were not good enough for the wife of Brett Carrington, it had to be expensive silks and cloud-like chiffons, as well as lacy underwear she would never have dared to buy because of the phenomenal price.

There was no time to brood about her decision, for Aunt Emma involved her in the wild rush of preparing for the expected guests. At night Samantha slept dreamlessly from sheer exhaustion, a fact which saved her many hours of futile anxiety.

She saw very little of Brett during this time, and not even the glittering diamond ring he had placed on her finger succeeded in disturbing or disrupting her unnatural composure. Not once did he subject her to unwanted intimacies, but at all times remained completely impersonal, almost aloof. Perhaps this was why she had become enmeshed in a web of total unreality, behaving with an unnatural calm acceptance that at times exasperated Aunt Emma.

An ecstatic letter arrived from Gillian in which she apologised for the part she had played in Brett's plans, but stating that she was happy things had turned out for the better seeing that Samantha was marrying Brett.

It was a letter that left Samantha strangely unmoved at the time, although it surprised her to discover how swiftly news travelled.

Brett gave her more freedom during those few weeks, placing the Mercedes at her disposal for trips into Bosmansvlei, the quaint little town that served the farming community. Everyone appeared to know her, or know of her. It was embarrassing at times, although it made her feel less like a stranger when she did the odd bit of shopping that did not required a trip to Port Elizabeth. She should have known, too, that in a small town like Bosmansvlei everyone knew everything about everyone else in the town as well as the surrounding district.

The people were friendly, jovial and welcoming. To them she was the future wife of Brett Carrington; someone of importance. If only they knew how little difference it made to her, and of the dead ashes in the bruised heart she was offering, by force, to the most respected man in their community. Would they still think so highly of her? she wondered cynically.

Meisie, the grey mare, began to look forward to her almost daily outings, and the lump of sugar Samantha invariably carried in the pocket of her jodhpurs. Brett seldom accompanied her on these rides across the veld now that she was capable of managing Meisie with confidence.

She was out early one morning on the mare, exploring the farm, when she discovered a cottage almost hidden among the trees not far from the main homestead. Curiosity made her venture closer and to her delight she saw what she had always secretly wished for herself. A cottage with an ivy creeper trailing along the walls, a carefully tended garden, not as elaborate as the one at the homestead, but with a pleasant, restful atmosphere that gave one the impression that loving hands had planted each seedling as well as caring for the roses that flowered so abundantly.

'Hello there!' A young woman appeared around the side of the cottage, her auburn hair tied back in a pony-tail, an apron tied about her waist, and a smile on her slightly rounded face. 'You must be Mr Carrington's fiancée.'

'Yes.' Samantha's hands tightened spasmodically on the reins as the woman approached the fence surrounding the cottage.

'I'm Louise Oosthuizen,' she introduced herself, her English heavily accented. 'My husband, Ted, is Mr Carrington's farm manager.'

Samantha stared at her in surprise. 'I had no idea that Brett had a farm manager.'

'Good heavens, yes,' Mrs Oostuizen laughed merrily. 'This farm is much too big for a man like Mr Carrington who can't spend all his time here. Ted has been here three years now, ever since Mr Carrington's previous manager retired.' She shaded her eyes from the sun with her hand as she glanced up at Samantha. 'I've just made a pot of tea, but it's rather lonely drinking it by myself. Would you care to join me?'

Her warmth drove some of the chill from Samantha's heart as she accepted Louise Oosthuizen's invitation and dismounted. 'By the way, my name is Samantha.'

'Samantha,' she murmured, her grey eyes appraising her unexpected visitor. 'A lovely name for someone as lovely as you.'

Samantha blushed at the compliment as she followed her into the cottage and sniffed at the pleasant odour of home-made bread and a mutton roast in the oven.

'You must forgive me if the house is in a bit of a mess,' Louise Oosthuizen continued pleasantly. 'We've only just returned from holiday and I haven't had the opportunity to see to everything yet.'

Samantha realised now why Brett had had to leave his other activities to spend a month on the farm. It was so that Ted Oosthuizen could take his annual leave with his wife and the little baby boy that lay kicking and gurgling in his pram in the kitchen. The chubby little fingers curled tightly about Samantha's finger as she leaned over the pram and, as the uncertainty passed, she was awarded a toothless smile that melted the ice about her heart completely.

'He's adorable!' she exclaimed, picking up the cuddly bundle and hugging him against her breast.

'And thoroughly spoiled because of it,' Louise laughed, setting out cups on the scrubbed wooden table and pouring the tea.

Sitting down to have tea with Louise's baby on her lap was an experience that uncoiled the tension within Samantha, and she felt relaxed for the first time since that fateful day she had agreed to marry Brett.

'It's time for his morning nap,' Louise said eventually, marching off to the room with the child. 'Don't go away yet, Samantha.'

Louise returned moments later. 'Now, with him out of the way we can relax more. Tell me about yourself, Samantha?'

'There's ... really nothing much to tell,' Samantha said hestitantly, withdrawing mentally from this friendly woman.

'Ted and I were beginning to think that Mr Carrington would never marry,' she continued amiably. 'Ted said he was much too particular about what he wanted in a wife, but whatever it is, you must have that something special he was looking for.'

A wary smile curved Samantha's lips and she hastily

changed the subject. 'I really had a cheek to call on you so unexpectedly, but I found your cottage quite by chance.'

'*Ag, nee*, I don't mind,' Louise set her mind at rest quickly. 'I get very lonely sometimes with no one to talk to except Ted, when he's home. Mr Carrington's Aunt Emma has been here a couple of times, and I've been up to the big house once or twice, but I don't want to make a nuisance of myself.'

Samantha understood perfectly how she felt and her tender heart softened instantly. 'Louise, will I still be welcome in your home after ... after Mr Carrington and I are married?'

'Yes, of course!'

'Will you come and see me as well? I think I'm going to find it just as lonely sometimes with no one near my own age to talk to.'

'It's a pity Nadine isn't still alive,' Louise shook her head sadly. 'She was always so full of fun.'

'Did you know her?' Samantha questioned tentatively.

'No, but the Coloured farm labourers who've been here for many years often talk about her.' Louise sighed heavily. 'She had that terrible accident just a few months before we came to Carrington's Post, and Mr Carrington has never been the same since then. They say he used to laugh more when his sister was alive, and the big house was always filled with music. Nadine played the piano beautifully, I believe, but Mr Carrington sold the big piano after her death, and now the big house is filled with silence all year round with not much happy laughter in those big rooms.'

Samantha digested this in silence, trying to visualise that other Brett who laughed without harsh mockery, and probably spoke to the sister he loved with a gentleness devoid of cynicism and barbed insinuations. She tried to see him in this role, and failed dismally.

'I believe there was some speculation at the time as to whether she committed suicide or not,' Samantha delved deeper into this delicate subject in an effort to get a better understanding of the man she was to marry.

'*Ag, man*,' Louise began, pouring them each a second cup of tea, 'I've heard that story too. Everyone seems to think there was a man involved somewhere. I can't say that this is so, but I wouldn't be surprised. *Ja nee!*'

Samantha had plenty to think about when she rode back to the homestead that morning. Was it possible that that lovely girl, whose photograph she had seen on Brett's desk, could have committed suicide because the man she loved had let her down? What reason had Brett to blame himself for her death if this was so, or had Aunt Emma interpreted Brett's behaviour incorrectly? People could be wrong, of course. Nadine's death might have been an accident, and nothing more. It was strange, however, that Brett and his aunt hardly ever spoke of Nadine. It was almost as though she had never existed, except for the framed photograph on Brett's desk.

Nadine remained an unravelled mystery; a mystery enhanced by Louise's disclosure that there could possibly have been a man involved in the reason for her accident.

Samantha sighed heavily as she left Meisie with the stable boy and strolled listlessly back to the house. She had met Louise Oosthuizen quite by chance that morning, but it was the only good thing that had happened to her for weeks. She liked Louise and, if Brett had no objection, she would not mind having her as a friend to call on from time to time when the need for company arose.

These three exciting Harlequin romance novels are yours FREE!

Lucy Gillen sets this romance among the wild lochs and mountains of Scotland. **"A Wife for Andrew"** is a touching account of a young governess, her dour yet compassionate employer and the children in his care who suffer at the hands of a jealous woman.

In Betty Neels' **"Fate Is Remarkable"** Sarah's "marriage of convenience" is dramatically altered. Just as Sarah was getting ready to tell Hugo that she'd fallen in love with him, a lovely woman from Hugo's past shows up...

In **"Bitter Masquerade"** by Margery Hilton, mistaken identity is the basis of Virginia Dalmont's marriage. When Brent mistook her for her twin sister Anna, she wondered if her love was strong enough to make up for the deceit...

In the pages of your FREE GIFT Romance Treasury Novels you'll get to know warm, true-to-life people, and you'll discover the special kind of miracle that love can be. The stories will sweep you to distant lands where intrigue, adventure and the destiny of many lives will thrill you. All three full-length novels are exquisitely bound together in a single hardcover volume that's your FREE GIFT, to introduce you to Harlequin Romance Treasury!

The most beautiful books you've ever seen!

Cover and spine of all volumes feature distinctive gilt designs. And an elegant bound-in ribbon bookmark adds a lovely feminine touch. No detail has been overlooked to make Romance Treasury books as beautiful and lasting as the stories they contain. What a delightful way to enjoy the very best and most popular Harlequin Romances again and again!

A whole world of romantic adventures!

If you are delighted with your FREE GIFT volume, you may, if you wish, receive a new Harlequin Romance Treasury volume as published every five weeks or so—delivered right to your door! The beautiful FREE GIFT VOLUME is yours to keep with no obligation to buy anything.

Fill out the coupon today to get your FREE GIFT VOLUME.

Three exciting, full-length Romance novels, in one beautiful book!

FREE GIFT!

Dear Ellen Windsor:

Yes, please send my FREE GIFT VOLUME with no obligation to buy anything. If you do not hear from me after receiving my free gift volume, please mail me the second volume of Romance Treasury. If I decide to keep the second volume, I will pay only $4.97 plus a small charge for shipping and handling. I will then be entitled to examine other volumes at the rate of one volume (3 novels) every five weeks or so, as they are published. Each volume is at the low price of $4.97 plus shipping and handling and comes to me on a 10-day free approval basis. There is no minimum number of books I must buy. I can stop receiving books at any time simply by notifying you. The FREE GIFT VOLUME is mine to keep forever, no matter what I decide later.

Please print clearly

C78 – 5R

Name

Address

City   State   Zip

Romance Treasury

Offer expires December 31, 1978.

Detach and Mail
Post Paid Card
TODAY!

The guests began to arrive two days before the wedding was to take place in Bosmansvlei's old stone chapel, and among those first arrivals was Samantha's father. As much as she blamed him for her unhappiness, be became her oasis in a sea of strangers consisting of relatives and business associates to whom she was forced to make a pretence of sublime happiness. But only Samantha knew of the mockery in Brett's glances which others interpreted as complete devotion. Beyond caring, she found it easier to ignore that which would have caused her pangs of misery and anger.

'I'm so glad you were able to shake off your infatuation for Clive,' her father said when they had a moment alone in the seclusion of the garden and, without noticing the veil of sadness in her eyes, he continued: 'Brett will make you an excellent husband. You always did need a firm hand to guide you.'

Bitterness engulfed her, but she forced herself to smile and hastily changed the subject. 'Are you happy in Cape Town, Daddy?'

'Very happy,' he assured her, pulling her arm through his as they strolled back to the house where tea was being served to everyone on the stoep. 'I miss you, of course, but now that I know you'll be settling down happily in your marriage I shall be more contented.'

Settling down happily in her marriage! The words mocked her ruthlessly, but she did not have the heart to disillusion her father. She would never lack money, Brett would see to that, but he would never be able to provide that spark of inner happiness that came only from loving someone.

The magnificent homestead was filled almost to capacity and in the crush of people no one appeared to notice the occasionally stilted behaviour of the bride and groom. The most pleasant surprise for Samantha on her wedding day was the arrival of Gillian Forbes and Stan Dreyer.

Gillian burst into her room that morning while Aunt Emma was helping her to dress and literally pounced on Samantha, almost hugging the breath from her lungs.

'Gillian, it's marvellous to see you!' Samantha exclaimed excitedly, checking swiftly to see that her dress was still intact. 'I didn't dare hope you would come.'

'Darling, when I received your invitation I made immediate arrangements to have this Saturday off, and so did Stan,' Gillian added, her green eyes sparkling.

'I think I'll leave the two of you alone for a few minutes,' Aunt Emma said tactfully, hesitating at the door. 'Only a few minutes, remember, or we shan't be ready in time to drive to the church, and Bosmansvlei is thirty kilometres away.'

Samantha sent her a thankful glance, but she sobered instantly as the door closed behind Aunt Emma's slender figure dressed in a prim pale blue suit.

'Darling, I'm so glad you realised in time what a shallow creature Clive is,' Gillian continued, gripping Samantha's hands. 'You are happy now, aren't you? Brett is such a wonderful man.'

'Yes, Brett is ... wonderful. He ...'

'Sam darling!' Gillian exclaimed anxiously. 'You've gone awfully pale. You're not feeling ill, are you?'

Samantha pulled herself together with an effort. 'No, I'm not ... ill. It's just that I suddenly realised the significance of this day. It's my wedding day.'

'But of course it is, silly,' Gillian laughed. 'You're having a slight bout of pre-wedding jitters, and every bride is entitled to that.'

'Yes, I suppose so,' Samantha nodded, forcing a smile to her unwilling lips.

'Sam, you look lovely,' Gillian sighed, stepping back to examine the expensive satin trimmed with fine lace and intricate beadwork along the neckline of the low-cut bodice. A single pearl pendant, a gift from Brett, hung about her neck and nestled against her creamy skin like a solitary tear. 'I always said you were beautiful, Sam, but today you surpass just ordinary beauty. Brett will be proud of you.'

A lump rose in Samantha's throat, but she was fortunately saved from replying by the timely arrival of Aunt Emma. Gillian kissed Samantha swiftly on her pale cheek. 'See you later!'

Aunt Emma passed a critical eye over Samantha when they were alone once again. 'Hm ... a little more rouge on your cheeks, I think. You're much too pale.'

Samantha turned away from the mirror and clutched at the older woman's arm. 'Aunt Emma, I'm afraid!'

'My dear child, Brett isn't a monster.'

'But I don't love him!'

Aunt Emma's eyes softened. 'I never loved my husband when I married him, and I couldn't have wished for a better man. He was so gentle and understanding that, after being married to him for only a few weeks, I was so madly in love with him that I couldn't imagine why I hadn't seen instantly that he was the only man for me.'

Samantha was startled by this revealing bit of information, but it did nothing to ease her fear. 'I don't think I ever want to love a man again,' she said firmly. 'I don't think I *shall* ever love again ... not the way I loved——' She bit her lip, unable to say the name of the one whom she had come close to despising.

'You *will* love again, Samantha,' Aunt Emma insisted quietly, 'but this time it will be a mature love that will be lasting for all time.'

'I could never love Brett!'

'Love often kindles love, my dear,' Aunt Emma continued confidently. 'Has it never occurred to you that Brett might be in love with you? Have you never thought it strange that, after remaining a bachelor for so long, he should have left no stone unturned to make you his wife?'

Samantha quivered inwardly, rejecting this suggestion instantly, yet finding the idea intriguing enough to allow her thoughts to linger on it for some time. Long enough, in fact, to sustain her on the long journey to Bosmansvlei and the slow walk down the isle on her father's arm. It was when she saw Brett, tall and distinguished in his dark suit, that her fears returned. His dark hair was brushed back severely, and those unusual brown eyes never left hers from the moment she entered the church. Broad-shouldered and so infinitely masculine, he was every girl's dream of a perfect husband, yet Samantha could not help wishing herself millions of kilometres away at that moment. He appeared so cold and remote that she instantly discarded Aunt Emma's foolish suggestion that he might love her.

James Little raised the frothy veil from his daughter's face and kissed her raised lips. She noticed the film of tears in his eyes and swallowed violently as a lump rose to her throat, but she instantly regained her composure as Brett took her hand and slipped it through his arm. She glanced at him surreptitiously as the murmurs of the guests subsided and marvelled at his apparent calmness. Did nothing ever unnerve him?

His eyes met hers unexpectedly and, unable to tear her glance from his, she saw a flicker of admiration in their depths and something else which she was unable to define in that brief moment before he returned his glance swiftly to the clergyman who was clearing his throat, indicating that the ceremony was to begin.

Panic seized her at that moment. She was to become Brett's wife on this warm April morning, and it was too late to turn back the clock, or to wish she had never entered into this crazy agreement. A tremor shook through her and Brett's hand closed instantly over hers where it lay on his arm. It was a strangely comforting gesture, very much the same as when she had wept in his arms after learning of Clive's marriage. She had been aware of his inner strength on that occasion, just as she was made aware of it now, and she knew quite suddenly that, even if he did not have her love, he had her respect.

At Brett's request there was no reception, merely a buffet lunch and something to drink at the homestead for those who had travelled far and still had to return to their homes that same day. Their suitcases were packed and, after snatching a bit to eat, Brett and Samantha were given a send-off by the farmhands as they prepared to fly to Port Elizabeth on the first leg of their journey to Mauritius. It was touching to see the happiness of these Coloured people as they danced and sang for their 'Master Brett' and his wife on their wedding day. It was a gesture that brought Samantha close to tears.

The added weight of Brett's wedding ring on her finger, as well as her engagement ring, made her glance at it several times during their flight. In the rush to change into something more suitable she had had only a few moments to spend alone with her father, for which she was thankful, as it merely brought a lump to her throat at having to say goodbye to him again.

Brett kept up a flow of easy conversation as they transferred themselves and their luggage from his small aircraft to the Durban-bound Boeing, never giving her the opportunity to consider her nervous state. He was being a perfect companion, behaving very much like a man who was taking a girl out for the first time.

After changing flights once more at Durban they arrived at Mauritius late that afternoon and took a taxi directly to their hotel on the beach-front. Brett had acquired a suite with a private dressing-room and bath-room, and the view from the bedroom looked directly on to the picturesque beach with its tall palms.

'I've arranged for us to have dinner in the main dining-room,' he told her after they had unpacked their suitcases. 'I thought it would be preferable to have people around us this evening instead of spending it alone.'

His lips twisted into a wry smile as she stammered her thanks, but he did not pursue the subject and merely waited calmly while she checked her make-up before they left the suite and took the lift down to the ground floor. Brett ordered wine before dinner, but Samantha could not bring herself to take more than a few sips. The night lay dark and frightening before her and, no matter how much she tried, she could not rid herself of the alarming thought that she had to spend the night alone with Brett. He was her husband, and yet she dreaded the thought that he should touch her. Oh, God! What was she going to do?

Struggling through that superb dinner was a night-mare she thought she would never forget, and when they finally returned to their suite her hands were cold and clammy with tension and nerves. She was being silly, she told herself, but she could not help it.

Brett displayed amazing diplomacy by leaving her at the door with the excuse that he needed to buy cigar-ettes, and Samantha was left alone to wash and change into the frothy lace nightgown Aunt Emma had insisted she should buy for her honeymoon. It was far removed from the choice she would have made, for it was too flimsy and revealing. Her cheeks burned with mortification at the thought that Brett would have to see her in it, and she hastily pulled on the silken powder-blue robe which had been an unexpected going-away gift from her father.

She jumped violently as the door opened and Brett, still fully dressed, entered the room. Her heart was hammering so wildly that for a moment she had difficulty in breathing.

Brett's glance swept over her momentarily and a smile of satisfaction curved his lips. He gestured towards the two glasses and the bottle of champagne in his hands. 'With the compliments of the management,' he said, still smiling enigmatically as he placed them on the dressing table and proceeded to open the bottle.

She flinched nervously when the cork shot from the bottle, but Brett appeared not to notice as he filled the two glasses with the sparkling liquid. He drew a chair closer for himself and, as she subsided weakly on to the stool behind her, he placed her glass in her hand.

'To us, Samantha,' he said, raising his own to his lips.

'To us,' she echoed hollowly, sipping at the champagne and spilling some of the liquid before she could control the trembling of her fingers.

'Relax, my dear,' he said quietly, noticing her agitation and interpreting it correctly. 'I have no intention of pouncing on you and demanding my conjugal rights while you're in this state of nervous tension.'

Relief flowed through her veins like a heady wine and brought tears to her eyes. 'I'm sorry, Brett, just ... give me a little time.'

'I'll give you all the time you want. I can wait.' The

colour flowed back into her cheeks as she raised her glance to his. His expression was unfathomable, but there was a slightly cynical smile playing about his firm lips as he answered her unspoken query. 'There's a couch in the dressing-room. It looks comfortable enough to be made into a bed.'

Samantha blushed profusely and lowered her glance, but her conscience pricked her severely. 'I'm sorry,' she whispered again, not daring to meet her husband's eyes.

'Stop apologising, Samantha, and drink up that champagne,' he laughed, but his laughter curiously lacked mirth. 'Let's make up our minds that we're going to enjoy this short holiday, and let everything else take care of itself.'

When he eventually wished her goodnight, the tension went out of her as she subsided on to the bed and began to cry. She cried with relief, releasing all the pent-up emotions she had suppressed consciously and subconsciously during the past weeks until, exhausted, she crept between the cool sheets and slept.

CHAPTER EIGHT

AFTER a tearful start to that sun-drenched week on the island, Samantha found herself relaxing under Brett's undemanding influence, and it became the laziest dream holiday she had ever experienced. They had nothing more strenuous to do than to spend their days swimming in the cool blue waters of the Indian Ocean or languishing on the glistening sands, soaking up the sun while the island children amused them by clambering expertly up the stems of the tall palm trees.

The nights on Mauritius were warm and scented and they invariably had their evening meals served on the trellised balcony leading off their suite, after which they would stroll along the almost deserted beach while it was bathed in moonlight. Everything was so perfectly right for a romantic honeymoon that Samantha's heart ached inexplicably when she allowed herself to dwell fleetingly on that subject. Had Brett purposely chosen this island with that thought in mind? she wondered distractedly. Had he hoped that the romance of the island might influence her?

It was futile to dwell on these thoughts, since they merely served to make her withdraw further from Brett, instead of bringing them closer. Despite the unnatural circumstances of their marriage, Brett was surprisingly attentive, but the impenetrable wall between them remained firmly intact. Holding hands while they strolled on the beach seemed to come naturally, and when he occasionally kissed her lightly on the lips, she found it a pleasing experience instead of repulsive. She became accustomed to seeing his dark hair lying across his fore-head in an unruly fashion after a swim, and began to admire the muscular fitness of his tanned body.

Samantha, too, had acquired a deep golden tan by the end of that week, and she found herself wishing that their stay could be prolonged, for she was beginning to discover things about her husband that intrigued her. Beneath that harsh exterior there was a gentleness she seldom saw and, behind his mockery, a vulnerability that left her with the tantalising thought that, if she wanted to, she could penetrate his defence and dis-cover the real Brett Carrington. But, like all similar thoughts, these were instantly disposed of.

Samantha spent their last day on the beach, soaking up the sun while Brett went for a swim. It was peaceful lying there, listening to the sound of the waves break-ing on the shore, and the laughter of the children as they built sandcastles only to have them dashed away by the sea. Now, as she watched Brett coming towards her across the warm sand, she was not unaware of the admiring glances women sent him as he passed. Inex-plicably her own glance sharpened, taking in the broad shoulders and the rough dark hair, now damp and clinging to his muscular chest. She lowered her gaze to the slim hips and the rippling muscles in his thighs and calves, for the first time experiencing a feeling of pleas-ure at the sight of him.

'You should have come for a swim instead of lazing about here in the sun,' he said, drying himself vigor-ously with his towel before lowering himself on to the sand beside her. His eyes sought hers then and they were gently mocking. 'Did you miss me?'

'Would it flatter your ego if I said yes?' she asked lightly, by now quite used to his teasing, often mocking manner.

'It would at least be a sign that all was not in vain.'

Samantha froze instantly, growing hot under his direct scrutiny. It was the first time he had referred in any way to their relationship. She avoided his eyes, but his hand was beneath her chin and she was forced to meet his glance.

'Don't take everything I say so literally,' he said. 'I was merely teasing.'

Ashamed of herself for reading more into his remark than was intended, she grasped his hand in both of hers and pressed it against her cheek, uncaring as to how he interpreted her actions. 'Forgive me, Brett. You've been very kind to me and I haven't exactly been a model wife. If you think that it hasn't troubled me, then you're wrong. I——'

'Forget it,' he interrupted her stilted speech and, not caring who saw them, he kissed her on her unguarded lips. 'I told you I would wait, and at the moment we have enough on our hands trying to get to know each other.'

With that the subject was closed and Samantha was filled with intense relief. She needed time; time to adjust and to come to terms with the demands he would eventually lay upon her.

Settling into the homestead's plush white Master Suite with its gold trimmings was accomplished without any traumatic experience. Brett moved into the dressing-room without a murmur while Samantha had the main bedroom with its enormous four-poster bed to herself.

Taking over the running of that vast household under Aunt Emma's guidance was a far more difficult task, but Aunt Emma was adamant that Samantha should learn all there was to know as soon as possible. It was time she took a well-earned rest, she explained laughingly.

For Brett, the holiday was over in every respect. The relaxed manner disappeared behind the cool, aloof exterior of the business man who divided his time between city and farm. Samantha soon discovered that he appeared to have an inexhaustible supply of energy for every task he undertook, and that he never became ruffled when problems arose. She realised too, why his farm labourers followed his instructions so diligently, for he was always fair and prepared to listen to whatever they had to say.

As time passed she gradually became accustomed to his timely and often untimely invasion of her privacy. To see him emerging from the shower with his hair damp and tousled, and with nothing more than a towel fastened about his waist, was no longer unusual or embarrassing to her, but quite natural. He made a practice of entering her room at night before retiring, and it soon became a pleasant interlude she looked forward to when he was not in the city. They would talk about what had transpired that day, discussing incidents of importance, or sometimes maintaining a companionable silence while he smoked a last cigarette before retiring. Just before he left her on these occasions he would brush his lips against her cheek, a fatherly gesture that made her feel like a child instead of the woman she was and, as a woman, she began to reject the set pattern of her life.

It came as almost a shock to realise how rarely she thought of Clive during that time, and when she did, it was without pain or regret. Her experience had taught her to be wary of men with glib tongues and polished manners that smacked of insincerity. She found instead that she longed for Brett's company, the sound of his voice, the often accidental touch of his hand. At times she caught herself listening for his light step, the brief laughter that occasionally broke from him when he found something amusing and, most of all, she became inexplicably aware of a longing to feel those strong arms about her ... a yearning that usually left her shaken and confused.

Taking over the reins as mistress of Carrington's Post still left Samantha plenty of free time, for Brett's staff had been competently trained by Aunt Emma who, after relinquishing her duties, spent more time catching up on her letter writing and crocheting as the winter chill set in. Brett continued with his frequent trips to the city, staying away a few days each time, and taking with him the vital spark that kept Samantha on her toes. She missed him on those occasions, she could not deny it, but each time he returned from these trips he seemed further removed from her than before.

'Why don't you ask him to take you with him next time?' Louise Oosthuizen suggested one morning when Samantha rode out to have tea with her in the cottage, and that was exactly what she did when she found Brett in his dressing-room shortly after lunch one day. There was a peculiar tightening in her chest when she noticed the open suitcase on his bed.

'Take me with you,' she begged impulsively.

'Why?'

'Well, I ... could do some window-shopping in Port Elizabeth for a change, or——'

'You must think I'm a fool!' he rounded on her harshly, his glance stripping her of every vestige of confidence. 'Do you think I don't realise that while my hands will literally be tied with business affairs during the day, it will leave you free to spend your time with Clive Wilmot, when and where you please?'

'That's a vile thing to say!' she burst out furiously, despising herself for not having the nerve to admit that her reason for wanting to go with him was to be near him, and not Clive as he thought.

'Perhaps not so vile when you stop to consider,' he continued, towering over her as she gasped and fell back against the wall. 'Do you think I haven't noticed that distant look in your eyes when you're anywhere but here with me? You flinch whenever I touch you and, when the conversation becomes too personal, you shy away, like a frightened filly. I dare say if I were Clive you'd soon experience a few warm-blooded emotions.'

'That's not true! I know I asked you to give me time——'

'Time!' he interrupted with an exclamation of disgust, and she trembled at the flame of anger in his eyes. 'We've been married for two months, Samantha, and for two months I've left you alone. I'm going to be away for two weeks on this trip, but before I go I want to leave you with something to think about. When I return, Samantha, you and I are going to have to come to terms with our marriage. You're my wife, and it's high time that you begin to fulfil your wifely duties. Do I make myself clear?'

'Perfectly clear,' she could have said, but not a sound passed her quivering lips. She just stood there, clutching at the wall for support and dying slowly by inches as his glance swept over her with an insolence that set her heart pounding and the blood rushing to her head. She had the weirdest feeling that he was mentally stripping her of every article of clothing, and that there was absolutely nothing he did not know about her.

She shivered uncontrollably and, seeing this, Brett's lips tightened harshly as he turned away to close the lid of his suitcase. 'I've been very patient with you, Samantha, but I shan't be patient much longer. Forget about Clive. He belongs to someone else, and *you* belong to *me*.'

'You make me feel like something you bought at a bazaar,' she managed, her voice edged with bitterness.

He turned to her then and she noticed for the first time the lines of weariness etched between nose and mouth, the grey hair at his temples appearing more prominent as well. An emotion she could not explain caught at her throat while she felt herself drowning in the dark pools of his eyes.

'Given the opportunity, Samantha, I could make you feel like the woman you ought to be instead of the confused child you are.'

Long after he had gone those words still rang in her ears, taunting her, exciting her, and leaving her to wonder. When she had first met Brett she had realised that he had the ability to make any woman feel that she was cherished and important to him. His total lack of interest in women, except the one he was with, added to his magnetic personality. She had seen the way other women looked at him but, if Brett had noticed, he had given no sign of it.

She was not immune to his lovemaking. She could recall vividly two instances when she had found it extremely difficult not to succumb to the demands of her own emotions which he had so cleverly aroused. Would it therefore be so difficult to merely give rein to her feelings and allow Brett to have his way?

Taking such cold-blooded stock of herself was something new to Samantha. It horrified her, yet she knew that the time had come to force herself to take a look at herself dispassionately and to analyse each dissected part of her mind and heart.

Brett had given her two weeks to think about it, and that was exactly what she would have to do. There could be no running away now; no escaping what lay before her. Brett was her husband and she should have realised sooner that he was not the kind of man who would be satisfied with the abnormal life they had been living. He was vibrantly virile and his demands would have to be met ... soon!

There was no one she could turn to for advice at that moment. As far as Aunt Emma was concerned their marriage was quite normal, if grossly undemonstrative, and she would never dream of discussing her personal problems with Louise Oosthuizen. Louise and Ted, a stocky, tawny-haired man whom she saw occasionally when he called on Brett, were ideally happy in their little cottage with their baby son. They were simple, down-to-earth folk, who would most likely be shocked rigid to learn the true facts about Brett and herself. No, this was something she would have to sort out for herself, or heaven help her when Brett finally returned.

Samantha had plenty of time to think during Brett's absence, for she went down with a bad bout of influenza and was forced to spend several days in bed, a luxury she did not welcome at that time, since her thoughts were becoming more confused as time progressed. Aunt Emma must have telephoned Brett to tell him that she was ill, for he telephoned every evening to inquire after her health and continued to call even after the doctor had given her permission to leave her bed. The telephone had been placed beside her bed for these nightly calls, but they never spoke for more than three minutes at a time. Brett's queries were as impersonal as her replies, but after each call she was left weak and tearful, torn between the longing to see him again and the fear of what would eventuate.

'You're not well enough yet to stay up all day,' Aunt Emma remarked with concern when she found Samantha weeping into her pillow one evening.

Samantha dashed away her tears and argued to the contrary, but Aunt Emma was adamant that she could rest for an hour each morning and afternoon until she had completely recovered.

'Aunt Emma,' Samantha began tentatively when she had composed herself enough to speak coherently, 'tell me, what is love?'

Aunt Emma looked at her strangely for a moment befor she lowered herself on to the bed and took hold of Samantha's hands where they lay listlessly above the covers.

'Loving, my dear, means longing to be with the person you care for, wanting to please him and finding joy in the things you do for him. It also means that you're proud of the one you love; proud of the way he walks and talks. But, above all else, it's the desire to give of yourself; to give of your warmth and understanding when your husband most needs it.' She held Samantha's troubled glance for some time before asking: 'Are you discovering, my dear, that you're beginning to love Brett in that way?'

Samantha drew a shuddering breath. 'I don't know— I think so. Oh, Aunt Emma, I'm so confused!'

'Let me ask you this question. Do you still care for Clive Wilmot?'

'No!' The vehemence of her swift reply surprised even herself. 'When I think back now I can see so many flaws in his character which I was too blind to see at the time.'

'We all have flaws in our characters,' Aunt Emma reminded her gently.

'Not Brett,' Samantha retorted swiftly, colouring

profusely when she realised what she had said, but nevertheless continuing. 'There's no comparison between Clive and Brett. Brett is strong and dependable. He can be harsh when necessary, and ... gentle when he chooses. He'll never fail those who need him.'

'And you need him,' Aunt Emma concluded quietly.

Samantha stared at her blankly for a moment until those quietly spoken words penetrated her troubled mind. It was then that a strange new excitement stirred warmly inside her, bringing a light to her eyes which, moments before, had been dull and lifeless.

'Yes, I need him. Oh, Aunt Emma, how could I have been so stupid not to realise what was happening to me? How could I have been so blind?'

A smile kindled in the eyes of the older woman. 'Perhaps you were too busy ruling your life with your mind instead of letting your heart take over.'

The truth in that remark was like a stunning blow. Why had she not thought of it before? She had been so busy arguing away her emotions that she had never given herself a chance to feel anything. She had wanted love to come to *her*, instead of trying to meet it half way.

Love! Yes, this was love. With Clive she had been in love with love. She had thought romance and Clive had provided it with his suave, easy manner and his passionate innuendoes. Yet, when he had pleaded for a more intimate relationship, she had been repulsed. Now, knowing that she loved Brett, she was no longer filled with horror at the thought of giving herself. She wanted his touch, his close embrace. She wanted to belong to him as a wife should belong to her husband and ... to have his children.

For some time after Aunt Emma had wished her goodnight, Samantha lay marvelling at her own stupidity. It seemed now that she had loved Brett almost from the very beginning. If she had not been so wrapped up in her infatuation for Clive she might have begun to realise what was happening to her. She might have understood why she had so readily allowed Brett to monopolise her life and to dominate her thoughts. The only thing that marred her happy thoughts at that moment was not knowing why Brett had made it his business to come between Clive and herself. Was it all merely to save her from entering into a disastrous marriage, or did he really care? He had told her once that she was the only woman he had ever considered marrying, but he never told her that he loved her.

'Love kindles love,' Aunt Emma had once told her, and it could work both ways. If her love for Brett was strong enough it must surely kindle a spark of love in his heart. No one can remain immune for long when they are showered with love ... not even Brett. Could he?

Brett's return to Carrington's Post was greeted with mixed feelings. The dam had sprung a leak in his absence and he had no sooner arrived when he was whisked off by Ted Oosthuizen to inspect the damage. Samantha's joy at seeing him again turned to apprehension when he scarcely acknowledged her existence in the rush to change into something suitable for traipsing through the muddy waters. He arrived late for dinner that evening, upsetting Aunt Emma who liked to have everything on time, and finally retired to his study looking alarmingly morose.

Nothing seemed to be going the way Samantha had planned, and she eventually went up to her room in a rather dejected frame of mind. It was some time after she had bathed and prepared herself for bed that she heard Brett's slow, almost dragging footsteps pass her door and enter his room. For the first time since she had known him, she sensed that he was tired, and her heart twisted with compassion.

She was restless and tense as she crossed to the window. The air was still and fragrant now that darkness had fallen over the Karoo like a cloak, hiding its arid beauty from her searching glance. The moon had sought refuge behind a cloud and the howl of a jackal in the distance sent an involuntary shiver up her spine.

'You shouldn't be standing in front of an open window on a cold night like this,' Brett's voice startled her as he spoke directly behind her.

With wild-beating heart she inhaled the pleasant odour of his shaving lotion as he brushed against her while closing the window, and she knew, without turning, that his hair would be damp from his shower. She was incapable of moving, every nerve tingling at his nearness, while the desperate longing to feel his arms about her became almost impossible to bear.

'Samantha,' he murmured, his hands sliding over her shoulders, their warmth penetrating through her silk robe and flowing like a current of electricity through her. She began to tremble and he released her instantly. 'Do I repel you that much?'

'You don't repel me,' she argued tremulously, keeping her back firmly towards him as she suppressed the desire to lean back against him.

'But I don't attract you as a lover.'

A pulse throbbed painfully in her throat. 'I never said that.'

'But that's what you're trying to imply.'

'Brett, you're putting words into my mouth,' she said in despair.

'How else then am I to interpret your actions?' he

demanded harshly, taking her roughly by the shoulders and turning her to face him. 'Answer me!'

Samantha stared up at him, her lips trembling and her eyes a luminous deep violet with suppressed emotions. Her robe had parted as a result of his rough handling and his eyes were aflame as they found the revealing cleft between creamy breasts. There was a fluttering in her throat and a wild upsurge of expectancy as she waited breathlessly, unashamedly willing him to take her in his arms.

'My God, Samantha, I want you,' he cried, and she was crushed against the length of him with a force that almost drove the breath from her body. His mouth sought hers with a demanding pressure that drove her lips apart while her heart leapt in response to every caress. When he finally raised his head his glance was tortured and torn with desire. 'You don't know what it's been like, having you near me and not being able to touch you.'

'Brett ...' she sighed against his lips. She slid her arms about his neck and pressed closer to him, offering her lips.

With an exclamation of triumph he plundered her yielding lips, his impatient hands sliding her robe from her shoulders to lie in a silken heap at her feet. Her breathing came shallow and fast when he finally lifted her high in his arms and carried her into the shadows of the bed. She could no longer think coherently, and neither did she want to. She was aflame with emotions and sensations that sharpened on desire, conscious for the first time of the need to satisfy the demands of her own body.

She felt no fear as Brett took her to the heights of ecstasy, merely a joyous desire to give as much as she was receiving. It was only later, while Brett lay sleeping beside her, that she realised with aching despair that he had not once said that he cared. No tender words of love had passed his lips, merely a driving passion that left no room for anything else.

Samantha stirred beneath the unfamiliar weight of his arm and, even as he slept, his arm tightened and drew her against the warmth of his body. Perhaps, she decided drowsily, it would pay to tread carefully for a time. Until he showed signs of caring, her own love must lay hidden in her heart. The realisation was too wonderfully new to survive Brett's mockery or the knowledge that her love would never be returned.

Samantha awoke the following morning to find that she was alone. Stifling a yawn, she stretched lazily and curled up beneath the covers once more, her thoughts turning instantly to Brett. Where was he? What was he doing? Would she see him before breakfast?

Anxious now to be with him, she bathed and changed into warm slacks and a woollen sweater, taking time with her make-up and brushing her spun-gold hair until it fell in soft waves around her face. Her heart was singing on that cold June morning with the frost lying thick and white on the veld until the sun melted it away.

'Where's Brett?' she asked Aunt Emma when she joined her for breakfast in the dining-room.

'He had breakfast early this morning and went out to supervise the repairs to the dam. If I know Brett, then he won't be back until this evening.'

Aunt Emma was right and Samantha had to swallow her disappointment. Brett did not return home for lunch, but arrived shortly before dinner that evening and went directly upstairs to shower and change. When he eventually came down to the dining-room, he was his usual cool, aloof self, and Samantha, confused and hurt, had to fight against threatening tears. It was almost as though nothing of importance had happened between them, and they were back to where they were before his departure for the city.

He excused himself eventually, saying, 'I've brought work home that needs attention,' and promptly disappeared into his study.

'Aunt Emma?' Samantha questioned helplessly, her eyes filling with tears she could no longer hold back.

'Men are sometimes thoughtless, child,' Aunt Emma said sympathetically. 'They wrap themselves up in their work and don't give a thought for anyone else. Don't let it upset you. He'll come to you later, and all will be well.'

Aunt Emma was right, for, later that evening, when Samantha lay snuggled up in bed, her mind in too much of a turmoil to sleep, her bedroom door opened and Brett stood silhouetted against the light from the passage. He hesitated when he saw that her light was off and, anticipating his retreat, she sat up swiftly and switched on the bedside lamp.

'Did I wake you?' he asked, closing the door behind him and placing a tray beside the bed. 'I thought you might like some cocoa.'

'I wasn't asleep,' she assured him swiftly as she studied him with a quick ache in her throat.

His shoulders drooped with fatigue as he sat down beside her on the bed, and she instantly quelled the desire to smooth away the lines of tiredness beside his mouth with her fingertips. Would she ever be able to hide the flame of love that now burned so steadily in her heart for this man? she wondered, her pulse rate quickening as she accepted the mug of cocoa from him, sipping at it while she observed him from beneath lowered lashes.

'Samantha, about last night——' he said eventually, looking at a spot above her head somewhere.

A tender smile quivered on her lips, but she controlled it instantly as she placed her empty mug on the tray and gave him her undivided attention. 'Yes, Brett?'

'Forgive me if I was rough with you,' he said hoarsely, meeting her hungry glance at last. 'I never intended frightening you.'

'You didn't frighten me,' she whispered.

'Do I take that to mean that in future you'll be my wife in every possible way?' His eyes passed over her like a slow caress and a shiver of delight surged through her, spreading like a ripple and filling her being.

'Yes.' Her voice was a mere thread while she blushed profusely beneath the ardency of his gaze.

'Samantha, you're so small you are almost like a child,' he said savagely, gathering her into his arms, 'but you're so very beautiful, and so infinitely desirable.'

Her lips parted beneath his as she slipped her arms about his neck and pushed her fingers through his crisp dark hair. She could feel the heavy beat of his heart against her and then, inevitably, the gentleness of those strong hands moving caressingly against her creamy skin. With an exclamation of delight she slipped her hands beneath his silk shirt and felt the rippling of his shoulder muscles beneath her fingertips as he threw the covers aside, the pressure of his lips and hands demanding an finding an instant response in her.

His mug of cocoa remained almost untouched in the tray, making way for more important matters such as a husband and wife discovering each other for the first time.

Samantha cherished every moment she spent with Brett during the weeks that followed. He was a demanding and exacting husband and lover, never allowing her to forget the power he wielded over her. She existed only for him, for his smile, however mocking, and his touch. He had ensnared her heart completely, bringing her to the full bloom of womanhood as she came to know the heights and depths of love.

Love! The only thing that marred her ecstatic happiness was not knowing whether Brett loved her, or was merely using her as an instrument to satisfy his physical needs.

With the advent of spring Samantha began to suspect that a new young life was growing inside her, and this was confirmed by the family doctor when he was called out one day after she had fainted. Brett was away at the time, but he appeared to be pleased when she finally confronted him with the news.

'You must take more care of yourself in future,' he said with unusual concern, lifting her on to the bed where she had been resting until his arrival.

'Brett, you are happy about this, aren't you?' she pleaded for assurance. 'You're not just saying so to please me?'

His glance was an instant rebuke. 'Do I ever say anything I don't mean?'

'No, but——'

'I want this child very much, Samantha,' he interrupted swiftly. 'But I want you to take great care of yourself.'

'Brett, stop thinking of me as a child!'

'I don't,' he assured her mockingly, sliding his lips along her throat to where a pulse throbbed in response. 'Not when I'm holding you in my arms like this and can feel your heart beating so fast beneath my hand.'

'Oh, Brett ...' she moaned softly, a sudden urgency taking possession of her as she moved against him. Her arms tightened about his neck, but he held back, his look of concern deepening.

'My dear, we must be careful.'

'Brett, hold me close,' she cried passionately, unexpected tears shimmering in her eyes. 'I promise I shan't break. Don't shun me physically now that I'm to have your child.'

'Shun you?' He looked startled for a moment and then, with a throaty sound, drew her wholly into his arms. 'Good God, Samantha, I could never do that. You know very well that at this moment I want you more than anything else.'

She tried to speak, but he silenced her effectively, her immediate doubts and fears swept aside as he set about proving her desirability.

CHAPTER NINE

REDECORATING the old nursery became a major operation. Paint and wallpaper had to be bought as well as new curtaining and carpets to replace the old. The flurry of plans being made and the excited gurgle from Aunt Emma at the prospect of having a child in the home caused many a raised eyebrow from Brett. It was difficult to know just what he was thinking, or how he felt about his whole household being disrupted to accommodate the expected baby.

Samantha grasped every happy moment with both hands, almost as if she feared it would disintegrate at any moment. Loving Brett the way she did brought its own pain; the pain of not knowing what lay in his heart, and the inability to reach him at times when he erected that cold, impenetrable wall between them. He appeared occasionally to lose patience with her and, confused and deeply hurt, her failure to understand made her plunge to the depths of despair.

Brett handed her a letter one evening while they were having coffee in the living-room. 'It was among my private post that came this afternoon, but I've only just noticed it,' he explained.

The handwriting was not familiar to Samantha and she ripped open the envelope, extracting the single sheet of paper. Her curious glance went swiftly to the name at the bottom of the sheet, and she froze instantly. It was from Clive!

'Samantha,' she read, frighteningly aware of Brett leaning against the fireplace, his dark eyes resting broodingly on her, 'How foolish of you to have married Brett Carrington. Didn't you know that he married you only to have an heir? If you don't believe me, then ask him about the stipulation in his father's will that states he has to produce an heir before he reaches the age of forty, or lose his inheritance. He's now thirty-nine.

'It is not my intention to upset you, but I felt you ought to know. Yours always, Clive.'

Samantha's face was deathly pale as she read the letter through once more before tearing it to shreds between her trembling fingers. There was a drumming in her ears that made her head feel as though it wanted to burst, while every word in that incriminating letter seemed to tear her heart to shreds. Could it be true? Was that all she meant to Brett—someone to produce the heir he so desperately needed to retain his inheritance?

'Was that letter from Clive?' Brett asked coldly, his face taut with anger.

Samantha nodded, unable to speak as her throat tightened with the pain of knowing the truth at last.

'What did he want?' Brett continued harshly, his eyes narrowed to slits as she rose on shaky legs to drop the pieces of paper into the fire.

'He ... wished us well ... with our marriage,' she lied through clenched teeth, drawing a deep breath to steady herself as she avoided his eyes and watched instead the flames rise higher in the grate as Clive's letter distintegrated into ashes.

Ashes! That was all she had left of a wonderful dream that one day Brett might love her. Oh, how stupidly naïve she had been!

'He's rather late with his congratulatory wishes,' Brett mocked her. 'Five months too late.'

'Too late! Five months too late!' she repeated to herself with rising hysteria. She was going to have Brett's child. His inheritance was safe—he had made sure of that!

'I'm ... rather tired,' she managed haltingly, turning away from the silent figure beside the fire. 'I'm going to bed.'

To her relief he made no effort to stop her and she made her way upstairs on legs that seemed unwilling to obey the commands of her numbed brain. Somehow she managed to undress and crawl into bed where she lay in a crumpled heap, allowing her aching misery to flow from her through the tears that appeared never ending.

She had no idea eventually how long she had lain there, but the tears on her cheeks had finally dried and the emptiness within her had become a lead weight she felt incapable of carrying with her through the future.

It was all so devastatingly clear to her now. Brett had married her merely to produce the heir he needed to enable him to keep his inheritance. Love was never involved. All that he had needed was a physical attraction to enable him to reach his goal ... and that goal was now accomplished. She was going to have his child. His heir! What happens now? she wondered tiredly. A slow degeneration of their relationship until they become like strangers living together, demanding nothing and expecting even less?

Oh, God, what a fool she had been! What an utter fool to have given her heart, her very soul, to a man like Brett Carrington. He had used her shamelessly to meet the requirements of his father's will and now, his mission accomplished, he would have no further interest in her. Indeed, he had so often shown that he had no lasting interest in her. He would, no doubt, take care not to show his true feelings until after the birth of the child, but once the baby was there it would all be over. The end of a foolish dream she had harboured of winning her husband's love.

Brett did not come to her that night, but slept instead in the dressing-room as he had done at the start of their marriage. His action indicated a clear break in their relationship which made the pain of loving him more acute.

It would be useless trying to make herself believe that she hated him, she realised that chilly spring morning as she stared at the empty space beside her on the bed. After a sleepless night she realised that she could not leave him either, for never to see him again would be even more agonising than knowing he did not love her. Life had become a vicious circle. There was no way out except to go on with the desperate hope that she would eventually come to terms with whatever the future had in store for her.

'I don't want you rush you, Samantha,' Aunt Emma said one evening, 'but I do think you should get the redecorating of the nursery done before you're incapable of attending to it personally. You have less than seven months to do so.'

'Perhaps you should go to Port Elizabeth. Bosmansvlei hasn't much to offer in that line,' Brett suggested from behind his newspaper.

'Yes ... I suppose so.' Samantha bit her lip thoughtfully. During the past few days they had acknowledged each other with a chilly politeness that brought a constant ache to her throat.

'Doesn't the idea appeal to you?'

'Well ... we could fly there and back in one day.'

'There'll be no flying for you at the moment,' Brett

insisted sharply, lowering the newspaper to glance at her sternly. 'I shall get Lucas to drive you there.'

'Lucas?' She felt a wave of disappointment sweeping through her. 'I . . . I thought . . .'

'I'm afraid it's impossible for me to get away at the moment,' Brett informed her dispassionately, disappearing once more behind his newspaper. 'It's lambing season.'

'I see . . .' Samantha glanced at Aunt Emma, but the older woman merely shrugged her shoulders, indicating that she was at a loss to understand Brett's peculiar behaviour. It was, however, a rather weak excuse on Brett's part, for Ted Oosthuizen was quite capable of handling the farm without him.

'I'll make arrangements for you to leave in the morning,' Brett said eventually, folding his newspaper and rising to his feet. 'My suite at the hotel will be prepared for you to stay overnight.'

'Brett,' Samantha said swiftly, clutching at his arm as he passed her chair, 'you won't change your mind about coming with me?'

'Surely I can trust you now, Samantha?' he said, raising his eyebrows mockingly as he carefully disengaged himself and left the room.

Aunt Emma let out an exasperated sigh as they heard the study door close behind him. 'Take no notice, my dear. Men are peculiar creatures at times, with peculiar notions.'

Samantha was not at all happy with the situation, but Brett's decidedly odd behaviour did not come as a surprise to her. He had lost interest in her, and the plans for the baby as she had thought he would. It could perhaps also be that he did not believe her explanation as to the contents of Clive's letter, and most probably thought that she had plans to strike up a new relationship with Clive. Would he care if this was so? she wondered distractedly. Or was he no longer concerned with what she did as long as the birth of his heir was ensured?

Aunt Emma excused herself eventually and went up to her room while Samantha remained for a moment longer, staring thoughtfully into the dying embers of the fire. Clive had certainly ruined her life with his supposedly well-meant information. It had been intentional and vindictive, but it could only be the truth, or Clive would not have been so bold to suggest that she confront Brett with his accusation.

When she crossed the hall on her way upstairs she saw the light beneath the study door, and knew that she would not rest until she had spoken to Brett once more.

'Come in,' he called in answer to her knock, and she stepped inside gingerly, closing the door behind her and leaning against it for support. Brett sat behind his desk, his raised glance sending a sudden chill along her spine. 'What is it, Samantha?'

She steadied herself and took a deep breath. 'Brett, I hope you're not thinking that I have any desire to see Clive again?'

His eyes narrowed slightly but his expression remained unfathomable. 'My dear Samantha, if you're entertaining such thoughts then there's nothing I can do to stop you.'

'That sounds funny coming from you,' she laughed without mirth, 'considering how you went out of your way to keep us apart.'

'That was eight months ago.'

'What's that supposed to mean?' she asked warily, dreading the direction her thoughts were taking.

'You can interpret that in whichever way you please,' he remarked, showing signs that the conversation was beginning to bore him. 'Take my advice, Samantha, and get to bed early. You have a long drive ahead of you tomorrow.'

Dismissed, Samantha went up to her room with a growing fear in her heart she could no longer ignore. It was over—Clive's letter had seen to that. It had made Brett doubt her, and it had shattered her hopes of winning the love of the one man who mattered above all else. She had trusted Brett implicitly, and he had let her down—something she had never thought him capable of. Now there was nothing left to live for except the child, which meant so much and yet so little to Brett.

Samantha moaned softly as a searing pain lodged in her heart. Dry-eyed, she fell across the bed and buried her face in her arms, the agony of failure too unbearable to think about. Brett would never ask her to leave; to him marriage was binding, but he had made it perfectly clear that she could expect nothing more than consideration and disorientated affection.

How strange, she thought when she finally went to bed. She had thought she would never get over losing Clive, but it had been accomplished without much suffering. Losing Brett would be a different matter entirely, for merely thinking about it made her wish for the oblivion of death.

She was still awake when Brett eventually entered his room. She heard him moving about and take a shower, but she knew he would not come to her. Whatever significance he had placed on Clive's letter, it had been damning enough to make him avoid her and, despite everything, she longed for his arms and his lips. Humiliation and anger had made way for a deeper realisation during these few heartbreaking days—no matter what he had done, she needed him. She would always need him.

Samantha awoke the following morning to find a cryptic note from Brett on her breakfast tray, and with unsteady hands she unfolded it.

'I'm sorry I couldn't wait to see you off this morning,' he had written in his bold handwriting, 'but I shall telephone you this evening. I've made all the necessary arrangements for your stay in the city. Take care of yourself. Brett.'

She read it through once more before crushing it in her hand, determined now to show Brett that she was unaffected by his behaviour. If he could be cool and aloof, then so could she. Never would she let him know how much she loved him, or how his callous behaviour ripped her heart to pieces. Never! From that moment onwards she would dish out as much as she received, and in kind.

The drive to Port Elizabeth was tiring, but they arrived at the hotel before lunch that day and Samantha was installed into Brett's private suite with its plush furnishings and gold drapes with a pomp and ceremony that left her gasping. When she tried to do away with some of the servants, Brett's manager appeared almost affronted.

'Mr Carrington's instructions were most explicit, Mrs Carrington,' he informed her. 'Nothing should be spared to ensure your comfort. The servants attending to you have been handpicked by Mr Carrington to attend to him personally when he is here, and they would be most dissatisfied if you don't give them the opportunity to do the same for you, Mrs Carrington.'

Faced with this argument Samantha was forced to relent. Her meals were served to her in the suite, doing away with the necessity of mingling with the other guests and, when she inquired, she was told that Lucas had been given accommodation in the servants' quarters in order to be at hand when she should need him. Everything appeared to be taken care of, leaving her free to do the shopping she had come for, but she could not help feeling like a novice when it came to handing out instructions.

With her shopping partially done that afternoon, Samantha sat down after dinner at the marble-topped writing desk and made a list of the items she still required. The faint sound of music drifted up towards her from the hotel restaurant and suddenly she was overcome with loneliness. She thought of the two other occasions she had entered Brett's suite, especially on that first occasion when he had invited her to dinner. She had been overcome with nervous anxiety at the time, overawed by the splendour of her surroundings and the forcefulness of her host. She had, at that time, still considered herself to be so much in love with Clive, but she knew now what it was to love someone deeply and passionately. She knew also the heartache of never being able to express that love for fear of being rejected. She was to have Brett's child, but it seemed now as though she would never have his love —a love she craved above all else in the world.

Overcome with self-pity and knowing she must fight it, she tried to concentrate on the list she was drawing up, but the longing for Brett became almost too much to bear, and she finally closed her eyes to ease the ache behind them. She jumped violently when the telephone rang shrilly beside her and, composing herself, she lifted the receiver.

'A gentleman to see you, Mrs Carrington,' the receptionist informed her. 'He says he's an old friend of yours.'

Samantha searched her mind for a possible friend,

but found herself unable to think of anyone else at that moment except Stan Dreyer. He could be the only male friend who would consider paying her a visit. 'Is it a Mr Stan Dreyer?'

'I'll inquire for you, Mrs Carrington.' The line went silent for a while and then the receptionist returned to the telephone. 'That is correct, Mrs Carrington. Shall I send him up?'

'Yes, thank you.'

How on earth did Stan know that she was in Port Elizabeth? she wondered suddenly after replacing the receiver. Could Brett, thinking that she might want company, have let Stan know she would be here so that either he or Gillian could pay her a visit? Surely not, she decided with a touch of cynicism. Brett would never think of something like that; besides, she was quite capable of doing her own telephoning.

A knock at the door interrupted her disturbed thoughts. She hastily put down her pen and went to answer it, but she was unprepared for the person who stood on the threshold. It was Clive, as handsome as ever, his boyish features displaying a certain weakness she had been too dazzled before to notice.

'Hello, sweetie! Surprised to see me?'

Samantha stood as if turned to stone. 'Clive!' she managed at last. 'But I thought——'

'That I was Stan?' he laughed knowingly as he brushed past her, closing the door. 'Yes, I'm afraid I made use of your inquiry because I had an idea that you might not want to see me.'

Samantha came to life then, glancing nervously at the closed door and wishing she had taken more care before allowing the receptionist to send up this un-wanted visitor. She was amazed also at the coolness within her. It was no use denying that she had dreaded meeting Clive again, yet now that she was face to face with him she felt not the slightest twinge of affection or regret that their relationship had floundered due to Brett's intervention. Clive had become more than a stranger—he was someone in whom she had not the slightest interest. An acquaintance long forgotten.

'I don't think we have anything to say to each other,' she said coldly, not inviting him to sit down. 'What do you want?'

'To talk to you, Sam, what else?' He stood with his hands thrust into his trouser pockets as he glanced about him with a cynical smile. 'Well, I must say you've done well for yourself. Landing a fish like Brett Carrington is what I call quite a catch.'

His inference that she had married Brett for his money infuriated her, but she managed to keep a tight hold on herself. 'Why did you come, Clive?' she asked.

He turned to her then with a display of sincerity that was unconvincing. 'I came because I had a yen to see you again ... for old times' sake. We were very close once.'

'How did you know I would be in Port Elizabeth this evening?'

'Brett Carrington is news, sweetie, and as his wife you get the same rating.' He flashed his old dazzling smile at her. 'You know how news gets around.'

His glance swept over her speculatively as though he were summing up her possibilities, taking in the expensive woollen dress that hid successfully the slight fullness at her waist, the diamond brooch Brett had given her as a wedding present pinned to the wide collar, and the soft leather shoes on her small feet.

Throughout this crude inspection Samantha remained perfectly still, but when his grey eyes met hers once more there was undisguised desire in their depths. Samantha went rigid with distaste.

'Does your wife know you're here?'

'My ... what did you say?'

Samantha had the satisfaction of seeing his composure shattered. 'Your wife, Clive,' she repeated calmly. 'I'm sure she won't like the idea——'

'But I'm not married!'

The silence that followed his emphatic denial was filled with conflicting emotions. It was Samantha's turn to stare at him in confusion. 'I ... don't think I understand.'

'Neither do I, sweetie,' he said agitatedly, peering down at her with renewed confidence. 'Is that why you married Brett? Because you thought I was married?'

'I ... I don't ...' she floundered, unable to articulate sensibly while her mind was in such a turmoil. Why should Brett have lied to her? Was it not enough that he had brought proof of Clive's escapades with another woman?

Clive was beside her now, but she was successful in evading his groping hands. 'Sam, sweetie, you don't realise how I've been pining my heart out for you.'

'You surely don't expect me to believe that, do you?' she demanded, placing some distance between them. 'If you're not married then what's happened to the dark-haired woman who lived with you in a beach-front flat and called herself Mrs Wilmot?'

Clive looked taken aback. 'Who told you that?'

'To use your own words, Clive ... news gets around,' she replied with a touch of cynicism.

'Sam, it meant nothing, I swear it. She was——'

'It really doesn't concern me.'

'Don't lie, Sam,' he laughed, advancing upon her with determination. 'Admit that it concerns you very much. You don't love Brett, you love *me*, and don't deny it.'

His audacity was almost laughable. He was so sure

that his fatal charm would have her falling into his arms that he was blind to the look of scorn that flashed across her sensitive face. 'Clive, I'm no longer free. I'm married to Brett, and that's the way it's going to stay.'

'That doesn't mean we can't take what happiness we can find.'

Samantha began to panic. 'I'm not sure I understand you.'

'Oh, come now,' he laughed knowingly as she side-stepped him once more. 'You're no longer the innocent young girl you used to be. Be nice to me, Sam. Let me stay with you tonight.'

'You must be mad!' she exclaimed in horror, seeing him for the first time as he really was—a man without scruples or sense of decency, and with the misguided idea that every woman was fair game. It was a moment of revelation that filled her with a relief so great that she would never be able to thank Brett enough for saving her from this obnoxious man stalking her about the room.

Clive bridged the gap between them with a swiftness that caught her by surprise. His arms tightened about her as she fought against him, his breathing laboured as his mouth sought hers. 'I want you, Sam. I've always wanted you, you know that.'

Filled with revulsion she managed somehow to evade his lips, but even as she did so she felt his hands fumbling with her zip. 'Let me go!'

'Sam, I've got to have you.'

'No!' Anger gave her added strength and she managed to free one of her hands, striking him a vicious blow across the cheek. Clive released her instantly, his ardour decidedly dampened by the stinging slap, and clearly startled by her unexpected attack.

'One would swear you were still a virgin by the way

you're carrying on,' he muttered with well-remembered petulance, fingering his cheek that was reddening rapidly.

'Well, I'm not!' she exclaimed furiously. 'But that doesn't mean that I have the desire to go to bed with any other man who comes my way. I'm going to have a baby—Brett's baby! And, for your information I'm very happily married and have no wish to seek pleasure elsewhere!'

'A baby? Well, what do you know!' he laughed nastily, recovering his composure swiftly. 'So Brett has made it after all.'

Samantha flinched inwardly as she struggled to control the shaking of her limbs. 'Yes, Brett has made it after all, and won't be losing his inheritance.'

Clive raised his eyebrows in surprise. 'So you got my letter ... and you don't mind Brett marrying you for that reason?'

'No, I don't,' she lied. Not for anything in the world would she let him know how much his letter had hurt her. 'I don't know what you hoped to gain by sending me that letter, but you may as well know that it makes no difference to me at all. I love Brett enough to overcome that stumbling block—if what you wrote is true?'

'Oh, it's true all right,' he said, observing her closely while he lit a cigarette with unsteady hands.

'How did you find out about it?'

'Well, I once heard——' He broke off abruptly and laughed briefly. 'Oh no, you're not going to catch me out that easily. Let's just say that I heard it mentioned once.' His expression sobered and became almost pleading. 'Sam, I did love you, you know.'

'You don't know the meaning of the word love, Clive. To you it means having affairs with women and dropping them when you've tired of them. To me, loving someone represents a more lasting relationship, and being true to one person only. Now get out of here,' she ordered contemptuously, 'and I hope I never have to see you again!'

'Take it easy, sweetie, I'm going,' he said defensively. 'If ever you should change your mind——'

'I shan't,' Samantha interrupted forcefully at his audacity, fighting a mental and physical fatigue. 'Good-bye!'

It was only after she had closed and locked the door behind him that she allowed herself to relax. It was perhaps just as well that he had come, she decided, sub-siding weakly into a chair, for now he would know, once and for all, that everything was over between them—that it had in fact been over a long time ago.

The telephone rang, interrupting her thoughts, and every nerve in her body reacted violently to the sound. It would be Brett. 'Oh, Brett, Brett, why did you do this to me! Why did you have to walk into my life only to break my heart in the way you have?'

Samantha raised herself tiredly and lifted the re-ceiver, a strange calmness taking possession of her as she heard his voice.

'I hope everything is to your satisfaction?' he asked after a peremptory greeting.

'Yes, thank you.'

'Did the journey tire you?'

'Not at all.'

Her own voice sounded peculiarly lifeless to her own ears and Brett must have been aware of this, for he said: 'You must take care of yourself, Samantha. Don't overtax your strength.'

Naturally, she thought cynically. She must not do anything to harm the child he needed so desperately. 'Oh, I shan't do that, Brett.'

There was a brief silence before she heard him ask: 'Has something happened to upset you, Samantha?'

What an understatement, she thought, her emotions bordering on hysteria. 'No.'

'You're tired, perhaps?'

'Yes.'

'Then I'll say goodnight, Samantha. Sleep well.'

The line went dead and she was left holding a lifeless instrument in her hand. It was so tragically symbolic of her marriage that she was on the verge of tears.

'Oh, Brett, why did you let me love you?' her anguished heart cried. 'Why couldn't you have told me the truth instead of letting me go on hoping?'

There was no longer any joy in this shopping expedition. The parcel of baby clothes in her bedroom was a bitter reminder of the function she had been chosen to perform. It was wrong to feel this way, she realised after a sleepless night. Her child would come blameless into the world, and it would need her love and attention. She *had* to prepare for its arrival as though nothing had happened to mar the occasion. It would, after all, be her child just as much as Brett's.

On an impulse she telephoned Gillian before leaving the hotel after breakfast. 'Could you get away from work and meet me at Garlicks for lunch?'

'I'll say I can,' Gillian agreed enthusiastically. 'Is Brett not with you?'

'No.' Through the window she could see Lucas waiting patiently beside the Mercedes. 'Gillian, I must fly. See you later.'

A fine drizzling rain fell that morning and, helped on by the south-easterly wind, it made shopping rather uncomfortable. Everything felt clammy to the touch, but Samantha was used to this kind of weather, the refreshing chill in the air whipping against her cheeks and bringing a touch of colour to them.

It was somehow comforting to ride through familiar streets, to walk into familiar shops, and to feel the pulsating city around her. It had been months since she had last walked these streets, for Brett never once offered to bring her with him on his frequent trips. Had he been afraid that she might meet Clive and learn the truth? A tantalising thought, but one that touched a rawness deep within her.

CHAPTER TEN

At twelve-thirty, with the last of her shopping done, Samantha dismissed Lucas and ordered him to return to the hotel with her parcels. But Lucas' brown face was almost indignant.

'But, Madam,' he argued. 'The Madam can't expect me just to leave the Madam here in the middle of Main Street? Master Brett will never——'

'Lucas, please, go back to the hotel. I'll have lunch in town and then I'll take a bus or a taxi.'

'Well, I don't know what Master Brett will say,' Lucas shook his head doubtfully.

'Master Brett need not know,' Samantha assured him, slipping out of the car just as the robot turned green. 'Don't worry so much, Lucas, nothing will happen to me.'

Lucas was forced to drive on while Samantha made her way swiftly to where she was to meet Gillian. She found a table without much difficulty and shortly afterwards Gillian arrived, windswept and drawing attention to herself as she almost shrieked with delight at the sight of her friend.

'Sam darling, it's good to see you,' she said, slipping into the chair opposite Samantha. 'You're looking a bit hollow-eyed, though. Pregnancy not agreeing with you?'

'It has nothing to do with my pregnancy. I'm really fine, I ...' She bit her lip nervously and fought against the tears that stung her eyelids.

Gillian glanced at her with concern. 'What is it,

Sam? I've never seen you this agitated before. Has something happened to upset you?'

'Yes, I . . . I have to talk to someone, or go mad! '

Gillian placed her elbows on the table and leaned closer. 'Talk away, darling. I'm an awfully good listener, but I don't guarantee my advice.'

Samantha sat for a moment, wondering where to begin and how to explain the confusion her life had become. It was not going to be easy talking about it but, with her father away in Cape Town, Gillian was the only other person who could perhaps listen impartially and give advice.

'What would you say if I told you I had reason to suspect that Brett merely married me in order to have an heir?' Samantha began, unable to disguise the quiver in her voice.

'Don't be silly! Brett loves you.'

'I doubt it very much.'

Gillian's glance sharpened. 'What on earth has given you the idea that Brett needed an heir so desperately?'

Samantha explained briefly, telling her of Clive's letter containing the damaging statement and his visit the previous evening, omitting nothing except his revolting suggestions that made her shudder to think what could have happened.

'You don't mean to tell me you believed Clive?' Gillian asked incredulously when she had finished. 'Really, Sam, you amaze me. You've always been so level-headed.'

The tears sprang instantly to Samantha's eyes. 'I'm so confused at the moment that I don't know what to believe.'

'That I can see,' her friend nodded sympathetically, but with a touch of impatience. 'Look, Sam, there's only one thing you can do, and you should have done it immediately you received that letter. Go home and confront Brett with this information, and I would like to stake my life on it that there's something wrong with the story Clive gave you.'

'Oh, Gillian, I wish I could believe that.'

'Cheer up, darling, it's not the end of the world yet,' her friend laughed, reaching across the table to squeeze her hand. 'There must be some explanation for Brett's behaviour, and I bet it's not at all what Clive has insinuated.'

They ordered lunch, but Samantha found it difficult to eat. There was nothing, however, that could put Gillian off her food. She was always at her happiest when she could eat, and the miracle was that she never gained an ounce of superfluous weight.

'By the way,' she said, working her way through a second helping of dessert, 'Stan and I are getting married in November and I shall expect Brett and yourself at the wedding. The invitations will be going out soon.'

'Gillian, I'm so happy for you,' Samantha exclaimed delightedly, her own problems momentarily forgotten as she shared in her friend's plans. It was only afterwards that she realised with a pang of regret how sadly her own wedding arrangements had lacked the enthusiasm Gillian was displaying, but she brushed aside these painful thoughts lest her heedless tears should fall in public.

When they eventually parted company, Samantha was forced to promise Gillian that she would follow her advice about confronting Brett. It was no use leaving something like that to become worse as time progressed, Gillian had said wisely.

Samantha took a bus back to the hotel, enjoying the short walk from the bus stop and the refreshing coolness of the rain on her hot face. She had to think, but she felt mentally exhausted and, by the time she had reached her suite, she was no nearer a solution than she had been when she had parted from Gillian in town.

She removed her hat and coat, shaking the few drops of rain from her hair, and only then did she notice the tall figure emerging from the deep chair beside the window.

'Brett!'

His name on her lips was a mixture of delight and despair while she marvelled at how arrogantly self-assured he appeared to be as he came towards her. She wished she could hate him for what he had done to her, but the heavy thudding of her heart mocked her and almost sent her rushing into his arms.

'What are you doing here? I thought——'

'I decided to fetch you myself. I've already sent Lucas home with your parcels,' he said smoothly. 'Sit down, you look exhausted.'

'I don't want to——'

'Do as you're told!' he instructed sternly, giving her a gentle push into a chair behind her. 'I've ordered tea ... ah, here it is.'

The tray of tea was placed on the small table between them and, surprisingly, Brett poured, neither of them attempting to speak until the warm liquid had succeeded in steadying her trembling hands.

'This excursion has been too much for you, Samantha.'

'Oh, for goodness' sake, stop fussing!' she exclaimed, rising agitatedly and turning her back on him to escape the intense scrutiny of his eyes.

'Surely a husband is entitled to fuss over his wife when she's going to have his child?' he said.

She was in the grip of such acute unhappiness that

she flinched under the impact and gripped the back of her chair for support. 'Clive was here last night,' she blurted out in an effort to shock him into some positive action.

'I see.'

Exasperated, Samantha swung round to face him, an angry flush of colour staining her cheeks. 'Is that all you're going to say? Aren't you going to demand to know how he came to be here, and what he wanted?'

There was a frightening calmness about Brett as he placed the delicate china cup in the tray and rose to his feet, placing her at an immediate disadvantage, for she now had to crane her neck to look up at him.

'Clive knew you were here because I dropped a few hints in the right places, and he took the bait just as I knew he would.'

She stared at him in absolute silence, unable at first to grasp what he had said then, as comprehension dawned, she clenched her hands tightly at her sides.

'How typical! Brett Carrington, the manipulator of people's lives!' she lashed out. 'Why did you want to make sure that we met?'

'I wanted you to get him out of your system, once and for all.'

Samantha drew a careful breath. 'I don't suppose it occurred to you that I might not want to see him again? That such a meeting was quite unnecessary?' Flames of anger leapt along her veins. 'Did you hope I would discredit you?'

'You're jumping to conclusions,' he said harshly. 'You're deliberately trying to find hidden meanings behind simple statements, and coming up with the wrong answers.'

'Am I finding the wrong answers?' she demanded cynically. 'If I am then you've given me no reason to think differently.'

'I'm losing patience with you, Samantha.'

'Perhaps, but why did you lie to me?' she asked, ignoring the look of warning in his glance.

'To the best of my knowledge I've never lied to you, Samantha,' he replied bluntly, thrusting his hands into his pockets. 'What in particular are you referring to?'

'You told me Clive was married.'

'And you've now discovered that the woman concerned was merely his current mistress?' he asked mockingly. 'My informant took it for granted that they were married when he found the flat registered in the name of Mr and Mrs C. Wilmot. Later, when I discovered this was not so, I didn't think it would matter whether I told you or not. You were by that time already my wife.'

'So you deliberately left me to think otherwise. After all, it had done the trick. I'd married you practically on the strength of that information,' she accused as a wave of bitterness engulfed her. 'How fortunate for you!'

Brett's eyes darkened with anger and his fingers bit into her shoulders causing a physical agony she almost welcomed. 'If you think I'll release you so that you can marry Clive, then you're mistaken.'

'I don't want to marry Clive!' she almost shouted, a look of distaste flashing across her face. 'He's the most revolting specimen it's ever been my misfortune to know!'

'Samantha . . .' He gave her a quick look and his hand slid across her shoulder to the nape of her neck. The caress brought her to the edge of tears, but she held them back.

'Please, there's something I must know.'

'What is it?'

Samantha shut her mind to the delicious tremors his caressing fingertips were producing. She could not relax until she knew the truth and only then would this terrible tension leave her. Her eyes were beseeching as she raised them to his. 'If in the past you haven't always been honest with me, be honest with me now, Brett. Please? I must know the truth.'

His lips relaxed slightly. 'Whatever it is that's so important to you, you can depend on a truthful reply.'

'Does your father's will stipulate that, if you haven't produced an heir by the age of forty, you lose your inheritance?'

His fingers ceased their caressing movements against the back of her neck and his hands fell slowly away from her as she held her breath and waited for the reply she dreaded.

'Who told you that?' he demanded harshly, and Samantha moved an involuntary step away from him.

'It was Clive who wrote and told me.'

'And you believed him?' he echoed Gillian's query.

'What else was I to do?' she pleaded anxiously, ignoring the cold fury of his glance. 'Is it true?'

'Yes, it is.'

There was a pounding at her temples as she expelled the air from her lungs and turned away from him wearily, her voice sounding strangled as she said: 'That's . . . all I wanted to know.'

She moved without realising it, stumbling into the bedroom in her anxiety to get away from this man who had used the foulest weapon in his possession with which to hurt her, and he had done so without the slightest sign of regret. She fell across the bed and dropped her head on to her arms as the tears came. Slow, convulsive sobs tore at her throat and racked her body even as she felt the bed sag beneath Brett's weight. He made no attempt to touch her until her torrent of weeping had ended, leaving her exhausted and clutching at the blue silk bedspread.

'Samantha, listen to me.'

'I don't think I want to hear more,' she said thickly, shrugging off his touch. 'I've heard enough.'

'You're going to hear more whether you like it or not,' he insisted and it was useless ignoring the authority in his voice as he pressed a clean linen handkerchief into her hands. 'Sit up, dry your eyes . . . and listen!'

Physically spent, Samantha could only wait while Brett lit a cigarette and paced the floor like a caged lion. A frightened pulse throbbed in her throat as she waited for him to speak, dreading to hear what he had to say, while at the same time knowing that nothing could hurt her more than he had already done.

He stopped beside her but still made no attempt to to touch her. 'I ought to take you across my knee for harbouring such thoughts about me, but then I can't blame you entirely. We haven't exactly been completely honest with each other in the past, and the lack of it was bound to cause misunderstandings.' His expression hardened. 'I'm to blame for that. I should have known better.'

Samantha felt as though she could hardly breathe as he turned away from her and resumed his pacing. Her eyelids felt heavy, her heart considerably heavier with doubt, confusion and hope clamouring through her. This was the moment of truth, she realised, but she cowered from it mentally, dreading what she might hear, while at the same time knowing that she would not rest until she knew it all.

'When I said just now that Clive's information was correct, I was not being completely truthful,' Brett began brusquely, his firm mouth unrelenting. 'My father had a notion that if a man wasn't married before the age of forty, he would never marry at all. He and I discussed his will at great length before his death. If I failed to produce an heir before the age of forty, then my cousin David's eldest son would inherit the business —but only after my death. But if, after the age of forty, I should marry someone young enough to produce an heir, that clause falls away and my children naturally inherit.' He crushed his cigarette into the ashtray and turned to face her for a moment, his expression cynical, yet slightly sad. 'It was simply meant as a precaution to keep the business in the Carrington family. It was something Nadine often teased me about. "Hurry up and marry," she used to say, "or you lose your inheritance." Obviously Clive took this seriously.'

Samantha was filled with remorse and intense relief, but she failed to see the connection between Clive and Nadine. Her eyes brimmed with tears, and she would have gone to him at that moment had she not realised that there was more to come.

'I'll tell you about Nadine, and I think that the best place to start is four years ago,' Brett continued, and she was instantly aware of an underlying anger beneath his controlled movements. He thrust his hands into his pockets and ceased his pacing to stand at the window with his back to her. 'My sister Nadine was young—your age now. She had led a very sheltered life and I'm afraid that, after the death of our parents when she was still in her teens, I may have spoiled her to a large extent. On one of her infrequent trips to Port Elizabeth she met Clive Wilmot and she was instantly swept off her feet.' The missing pieces in the puzzle were falling into place with shocking clarity. 'He promised her the world, but he was as much a fake then as he is now. He wanted to marry her, but when he discovered that I held the purse strings until she reached the age of twenty-five, and perhaps even after that if I thought it necessary, he dropped her flat.'

There was a savagery in his voice that frightened her and tore at her heart simultaneously. He was reliving painful memories that would have been best forgotten had they not become so vitally important to their future.

'It was not long before Nadine discovered that she was going to have a baby. She contacted Clive, begging him to marry her, but he made it quite clear that he had no intention of being saddled with a wife who had no control over her money, as well as a child. After that he promptly vanished without trace.' Brett turned to her then and she was surprised at the bitterness on that strong angular face and in the eyes that sought hers in the dimness of the room. 'Nadine couldn't take it, and before I could do anything to help her, she drove her car through the rails at the highest point on the Olifant-skop Pass at a time when I was flying back to the farm. When I found her farewell note it was already too late to save her.'

There was silence for a moment, while Samantha looked away. Then, 'Brett, I'm sorry,' she murmured inadequately.

'I saw Clive again for the first time in three years that evening you and I met in the garden of this hotel,' he continued almost as if she had not spoken. 'It was providence, but the desire to crush him was no longer there.'

Driven with compassion, she went to him. 'Why didn't you explain all this to me at the time?'

His lips twisted cynically. 'Would you have believed me?'

Samantha lowered her glance guiltily. 'I suppose not, but it might have made all the difference in the world at the time.'

'You were young and innocent, and in that respect

you reminded me of Nadine,' he said harshly, turning away from her almost as if he could not bear to have her near. 'I had to prevent you from making the same mistake, so I arranged for Clive to be sent away. I spent time with your father, getting to know him and discovering that we had a mutual concern—your involvement with Clive which could only lead to disaster.'

Samantha recalled vividly those evenings Brett had spent with her father. It was all so clear now that she was amazed at her ignorance at the time.

An involuntary smile plucked at her lips. 'So you practically abducted me, with the help of my father.'

'I couldn't keep Clive away from Port Elizabeth indefinitely,' he replied, his formidable back turned firmly towards her. 'At the same time your father had problems of his own to contend with. He really had no choice about taking that transfer to Cape Town, and he was torn between leaving you behind to fall into Clive's clutches, and taking an unwilling daughter with him.'

'I ... didn't know.'

Poor Daddy, she thought. How difficult she must have made it for him by her selfish desire to stay close to Clive, a man who was less than the dust beneath Brett's expensive leather shoes.

'There was only one solution to the problem. My farm manager, Ted Oosthuizen, was taking his annual leave, which meant that I would have to spend that month on the farm.' Brett turned to her then, his expression as formidable as his back. 'The rest you know.'

She was very conscious of the arrogant set of his head upon his broad shoulders, and the feel of his dark hair so crisp beneath her fingertips, but there was still something she had to know.

'Was marrying me part of the plan?'

'I hoped it would be.'

They faced each other in silence until the agonising question that hovered on her lips was finally uttered. 'Brett, why did you marry me?'

'Before I answer that, I shall ask you one question?' he said tersely. 'Do you have any feelings left for Clive?'

'No! He's the most hateful man I've ever met!'

He nodded his head as though satisfied. 'Good. Now the rest is up to you, Samantha.'

'Up to ... to me?' There was tension in the air as she met his glance unfalteringly. It was almost as if Brett were trying to convey a message to her which she was too frightened to grasp. 'Brett, if your reason for marrying me was not merely to save me from a fate similar to Nadine's, or because of your father's will, then ...' She faltered, unsure of herself in that supreme moment of sacrificing her pride in the strengthening knowledge of what she had to do. When she eventually found her voice she stumbled blindly through her confession while unshed tears threatened to choke her. 'Brett, I love you, and ... God knows I'll do anything to make you care ... just a little.'

'All you have to do is tell me again that you love me. It's what I've been waiting for all this time, to hear you say—Brett, I love you.' There was a new look of tender amusement in his dark eyes, and her heart leapt with joy as she found herself in his arms, her glowing face pressed into the hollow of his shoulder. 'You see, my darling, it didn't take me very long to realise that I'd fallen in love with you. I've loved you almost from the first moment I looked into your remarkable violet blue eyes, but I was too proud to admit it while I thought you still loved Clive.'

His lips found hers and she clung to him while she

experienced a happiness that pulsated through her with a force that left her weak. Nothing mattered at that moment except that sure knowledge that he loved her, and the unhappiness which had been her constant companion for so long seemed to evaporate into the mist of oblivion as she felt his arms tightening about her.

'Brett . . .' she sighed with melting warmth against his lips. 'Darling, I've been such a fool!'

'No, Samantha, my dearest heart,' he contradicted as a solitary tear found its way down her cheek. He brushed it away with his thumb and placed his lips against her closed eyelid. 'A little confused perhaps, but never a fool.'

'I've doubted you so much, and I've had such uncomplimentary thoughts about you.'

'I shall make you pay for each one of them, like this . . . and this . . .' He kissed her repeatedly with a growing passion that ignited a flame of desire within her. He trembled suddenly and with a groan released her. 'Samantha, I must know. When did you discover that Clive no longer meant anything to you?'

A tremulous smile hovered on lips still warm and tingling from his kisses. 'Long before I discovered that I loved you.'

'And when was that?' he asked suspiciously.

A delicate colour stained her cheeks but she met his glance unwaveringly. 'That time you went away and left me with an ultimatum.'

'Ah,' his expression lightened with gentle mockery, 'perhaps I should have delivered that ultimatum sooner!'

She was in his arms again, thrilling to the touch of his lips and hands and welcoming the storm of emotions sweeping through her. The rain lashed against the window panes, yet in her heart the sun was shining with a warmth that filled her being. Below their window the young willow trees were sprouting green leaves and, without intending to, she recalled Rosa's peculiar message.

'Rosa was right,' she whispered, inhaling the familiar smell of shaving lotion and tobacco as she slipped her arms inside his jacket, feeling the pleasant warmth of him as she pressed closer. 'The young leaves of spring are sprouting on the trees and I've found my star of happiness. You,' she added dreamily.

'So you did take it seriously after all,' he laughed against her smooth neck.

'Yes, I must have,' she admitted, trying to avoid those conquering lips a moment longer. 'The love I thought I had for Clive was like a handful of stardust. It was of so little substance that it trickled through my fingers unnoticed.'

'How can you be sure that you really love me?'

She held him off with her hands against his chest and felt the heavy beat of his heart beneath her fingertips. 'Brett, I love you so much that I was prepared to accept the fact that you married me solely to keep your inheritance, and I would have made the best of our marriage because ... to leave you ...' Her voice faltered while her heart was in her eyes for him to see the love she had so foolishly hidden from him. 'Darling, I would rather die than have to live without you.'

Samantha's son was born early one April morning at Carrington's Post. She had held the small pink bundle in her arms with awe-inspiring wonder until tiredness had overwhelmed her and she was forced to relinquish her cherished possession into the capable hands of the nurse Brett had employed to help with the baby until her strength was restored.

Brett came to her eventually after seeing off the family doctor, and he stood staring down at her for immeasurable seconds with a look of such deep devotion that it brought happy tears to her eyes.

'My darling wife,' he murmured, lying down beside her on the bed and gathering her into his arms. 'I died a thousand deaths these past few hours for fear I would lose you.'

'But everything went off so perfectly,' she protested, weak with happiness as she pressed her lips against his warm neck. 'Are you happy with your son?'

'My happiness is so complete at this moment, my darling,' he said in a voice vibrating with emotions as he traced a loving finger along the fine bone structure of her face. 'You've given me more than I ever dreamed possible.'

Samantha turned fully towards him and wound her arms about his neck. 'I love you so much, Brett.'

'My darling,' he whispered after a long and satisfying kiss, his glance teasing as he looked down at her. 'I shall have to get used to sharing you now.'

She laughed softly as she pulled his head down towards hers and pressed her lips against the greying hair at his temples. 'My husband, my love, my life. I shall always be there when you need me.'

She felt his lips, warm and tender against her own, and with a contented sigh she slept in his arms and knew that her dreams would be filled with the wonder of his love. A love that found an ever-increasing echo in her heart.

Have you missed any of these best-selling Harlequin Romances?

By popular demand... to help complete your collection of Harlequin Romances

48 titles listed on the following pages...

Harlequin Reissues

1282 **The Shining Star**
Hilary Wilde

1284 **Only My Heart
to Give**
Nan Asquith

1285 **Out of a Dream**
Jean Curtis

1288 **The Last of the
Kintyres**
Catherine Airlie

1289 **The Much-Loved
Nurse**
Pauline Ash

1292 **Falcon's Keep**
Henrietta Reid

1293 **I Know My Love**
Sara Seale

1294 **The Breadth
of Heaven**
Rosemary Pollock

1295 **Suddenly It
Was Spring**
Hilda Pressley

1353 **Nurse Lavinia's
Mistake**
Marjorie Norrell

1363 **Star Dust**
Margaret Malcolm

1365 **Hotel Southerly**
Joyce Dingwell

1368 **Music I Heard with
You**
Elizabeth Hoy

1371 **Dancing on My Heart**
Belinda Dell

1372 **Isle of Pomegranates**
Iris Danbury

1384 **Beloved Enemies**
Pamela Kent

1390 **Sugar in the Morning**
Isobel Chace

1394 **Nurse Sandra's
Second Summer**
Louise Ellis

1433 **The Pursuit of
Dr. Lloyd**
Marjorie Norrell

1435 **Scarlet Sunset**
Mary Cummins

1439 **Serenade at
Santa Rosa**
Iris Danbury

1440 **Bleak Heritage**
Jean S. MacLeod

1444 **Fond Deceiver**
Pauline Garnar

1449 **Dedication Jones**
Kate Norway

Harlequin Reissues

1456 **This Too I'll Remember**
Mons Daveson

1457 **Nurse Kelsey Abroad**
Marjorie Norrell

1464 **The Unlived Year**
Catherine Airlie

1468 **Yesterday, Today and Tomorrow**
Jean Dunbar

1473 **Silent Heart**
Louise Ellis

1475 **The Vermilion Gateway**
Belinda Dell

1477 **The Land of the Lotus-Eaters**
Isobel Chace

1478 **Eve's Own Eden**
Karin Mutch

1481 **Nurse Helen**
Lucy Gillen

1483 **Never Turn Back**
Jane Donnelly

1484 **On a May Morning**
Hilda Nickson

1638 **Pirate of the Sun**
Gwen Westwood

1643 **The Glory or the Love**
Margaret S. McConnell

1647 **The Sweet Spring**
Hilda Nickson

1651 **A Scent of Lemons**
Jill Christian

1652 **A Pearl for Love**
Mary Cummins

1654 **In the Shade of the Palms**
Roumelia Lane

1659 **A Parade of Peacocks**
Elizabeth Ashton

1675 **Song above the Clouds**
Rosemary Pollock

1677 **Stranger at the Door**
May Coates

1686 **Alpenrose**
Madeline Charlton

1691 **A Bowl of Stars**
Wynne May

1695 **That Island Summer**
Elizabeth Hoy

1697 **Healing in the Hills**
Ruth Clemence

Complete and mail this coupon today!